WORKBOOK

FUTURE

ADVANCED

English for Work, Life, and Academic Success

Second Edition

Series Consultants
Sarah Lynn
Ronna Magy
Federico Salas-Isnardi

Learning Expert
Lia Olson

Pearson

Future Advanced Workbook
English for Work, Life, and Academic Success

Pearson Education, 221 River Street, Hoboken, NJ 07030 USA

Staff credits: The people who made up the *Future Advanced Workbook* team, representing content development, design, manufacturing, marketing, multimedia, project management, publishing, rights management, and testing, are Pietro Alongi, Jennifer Castro, Dave Dickey, Gina DiLillo, Warren Fischbach, Pamela Fishman, Gosia Jaros-White, Joanna Konieczna, Michael Mone, Mary Perrotta Rich, Katarzyna Starzyńska-Kościuszko, Katie Sullivan, Joseph Vella, Peter West, and Autumn Westphal.

Text composition: ElectraGraphics, Inc.
Cover design: EMC Design Ltd
Audio: CityVox
Development: Blue Crab Editorial Services, LLC

ISBN-13: 9780134547640
ISBN-10: 0134547640

Printed in the United States of America

2 2021

Contents

To the Teacher

The *Future Advanced Workbook* has 14-page units to complement what students have learned in the Student Book. Each Workbook unit follows the lesson order of the Student Book and provides supplemental practice in grammar; workplace, life, and community skills; reading; writing; and workplace soft skills. Students can complete the exercises outside the classroom as homework or during class time to extend instruction.

The Workbook audio includes the readings from the Workbook so students can become more fluent readers.

UNIT STRUCTURE

Grammar

Grammar is practiced in contextualized exercises that include sentence completion, sentence writing, sentence scrambles, matching, and multiple choice. The lessons also reinforce the new vocabulary taught in the Student Book lessons. Some lessons include personalized activities.

Workplace, Life, and Community Skills

In the second edition, the Life Skills lesson has been revised to focus on workplace, life, and community skills and to develop the real-life language and civic literacy skills required today. Lessons integrate and contextualize workplace content. In addition, every lesson includes practice with digital skills on a mobile device.

Reading

All reading lessons have new, information-rich texts and a revised pedagogical approach in line with the CCR and ELP standards and the NRS descriptors. These informational texts are level appropriate, use high-frequency vocabulary, and focus on interpretation of graphic information. The readings build students' knowledge and develop their higher-order reading skills by teaching citation of evidence, summarizing, and interpretation of complex information from a variety of text formats.

Writing

In the second edition, a cumulative writing lesson has been added to every unit. This new lesson requires students to synthesize and apply their learning in a written outcome. Through a highly scaffolded approach, students begin by analyzing writing models before planning and finally producing written work of their own.

Workplace Soft Skills

Future has further enhanced its development of workplace skills by adding a Workplace Soft Skills lesson to each unit. Soft skills are the critical interpersonal communication skills needed to succeed in any workplace. Students begin each lesson by defining a soft skill. Then, while applying the lesson-focused soft skill, they review two situational judgment scenarios and assess how to best respond to each situation.

ADDITIONAL RESOURCES

At the back of the Workbook, you will find an answer key.

ORIENTATION

The Workbook, like the Student Book, includes an orientation for students. Before the students use the Workbook for the first time, direct them to To the Student on the next page. Go through the questions and tips with the students and answer any questions they may have so they can get the most out of using the Workbook.

To the Student

LEARN ABOUT YOUR BOOK

(A) Look through your book. Write the page number for each section.

Contents _____

Unit 1 _____

Unit 10 _____

Answer Key _____

(B) Look at page 72. Find *More than one answer may be possible.* What does this mean?

(C) How do you get the audio?

(D) Look at page 6. What does ▶ mean?

TIPS FOR USING THE AUDIO

Read the tips for using the audio.
- In the Reading lessons, use the audio to help you understand the articles.
- When listening for details, use the pause button so you can have more time to write and find the information you need.
- After you finish the unit, play the audio again and review the readings.
- Also, for more listening practice, listen to the readings when you are in the car or on the bus.

WRITING TIPS

Read the writing tips.
- Try to incorporate new and different grammar structures in your writing.
- Pay attention to punctuation, and make sure you use it appropriately.
- Organize your writing into paragraphs that focus on specific topics or ideas.

Use the Writing Checklist in the Writing lesson of each unit to check your writing.

The Power of Goals

Lessons 1 & 2: Grammar

A **COMPLETE.** Write sentences with a gerund or an infinitive. More than one answer is sometimes possible.

1. Joy / decide / consult / with the career counselor at her college

   _____

2. Min Hee / enjoy / help / patients in a hospital setting

   _____

3. Dan / need / clarify / some information before he makes a career choice

   _____

4. Ken / practice / talk / about his aspirations before the interview

   _____

5. Jun / did not / finish / prepare / for the interview until late last night

   _____

6. Yuki / would like / find / a job that has potential for advancement

   _____

7. Rosa / hope / major / in a field she finds inherently interesting

   _____

8. Feng / plan / build / her expertise by doing an internship

   _____

9. Jean Paul / expect / pursue / a career in engineering

   _____

10. Alexandra / agree / take / several different assessments before the interview

    _____

11. Amy / prefer / work / with a team

    _____

12. Ari / choose / focus / on instructional design

    _____

B **IDENTIFY.** Read the conversation between Joy, a college student, and a career counselor. Circle the words that correctly complete the sentences.

Mrs. Patel: Hello, Joy. Is this your first time at the TSU career center?

Joy: Yes, it's my first semester, and I'd like **to find out / finding out** more about careers.

Mrs. Patel: Have you finished **to take / taking** the personality and career assessments?

Joy: Yes. I'm hoping **to get / getting** some clarification about what the results mean.

Mrs. Patel: Absolutely. Let me look up your test results. It looks like you enjoy **to work / working** with children?

Joy: Yes. I volunteered **to help / helping** at a daycare last summer, and they decided **to hire / hiring** me in the fall. Helping children learn is inherently rewarding work, I think.

Mrs. Patel: That's great. You might want to consider **be / being** a teacher.

Joy: Maybe, but I'm concerned about the salary. I need **to pay / paying** my loans after college, so I'd prefer **to pursue / pursuing** something that pays well.

Mrs. Patel: Are there any other jobs that interest you?

Joy: I'm not sure, but I don't mind **to take / taking** risks. I also love challenges.

Mrs. Patel: Hmm. Your assessment indicates that you have good math skills. Have you considered **to study / studying** finance?

Joy: Not really. I don't like the idea of **to sit / sitting** at a computer all day.

Mrs. Patel: But there are many kinds of finance careers. Some involve **to work / working** with people. For example, you could become a financial consultant. They spend a lot of their time talking to people, explaining how to borrow or manage money.

Joy: That sounds interesting. I guess I would like **to learn / learning** more.

Mrs. Patel: OK, then you should start planning now. Do you intend **to study / studying** math?

Joy: Yes, I plan **to take / taking** a calculus course this semester.

Mrs. Patel: Good. I also suggest **to take / taking** a business course.

Joy: OK, I'll do that, too. I'll also keep **to think / thinking** about what I'd like to do. Thank you so much for your help.

A **READ.** What is a high-demand career?

Jobseeker

Home | Job-Seeking Tips | Articles | Blog | About Us

Finding a High-Demand Career

1 Sadie consulted with a career counselor at her school last week. The counselor gave Sadie career advice and skill assessments. Sadie learned that she has good communication skills and wants to help people. Her skill assessment showed that she should look for a "social occupation."

5 Sadie's career counselor suggested she look for a high-demand career that matches her interests and skills. A high-demand career is a job that is growing quickly. That means there are a lot of jobs opening in that field.

When Sadie looked for a high-demand career in the social occupations area, she discovered that a home health aide matched her skills and
10 interests. It is also one of the fastest-growing careers in the country. Home health aides help people who are sick or disabled. They work in clinics or in people's homes.

Sadie went online to find more information about available job openings in this field. She was excited to see there are more than 3,000,000 openings for home health aides in the country right now.

Sadie isn't alone. Thousands of people are looking for new careers every day, and thousands of employers are looking
15 for new employees. Are you one of them? Will you find a job in a high-demand career?

B **LOCATE DETAILS.** Read the article about Sadie again. Then read the statements and decide if they are true or false. Write the line numbers of your evidence.

	T/F	Lines
1. Sadie has strong communication skills.	____	____
2. Sadie's skill assessment says she should look for an "enterprising occupation."	____	____
3. The career counselor says Sadie should look for a job in a field with many openings.	____	____
4. There are more than 3 million openings for home health aides in the country.	____	____

C **INTERPRET.** Read the job description. Use the information to fill out the answers below.

High-Demand Career: Home Health Aide	
Wage	$24,500 / year $11.77 / hour
Preparation	high school diploma
Number of job openings in 2020	3,253,000
Number of new job openings in the next 10 years	1,185,800

1. The preparation you need to become a home health aide is a _____.

2. A home health aide usually earns _____ per year.

3. By 2030, the country will need _____ more home health aides.

4. In 2020, there were _____ home health aide job openings.

5. A home health aide usually earns _____ per hour.

D **GO ONLINE.** Find a high-demand career that matches your interests and skills. Fill in the chart.

- **My interests:**

_____

_____

- **My skills:**

_____

_____

High-Demand Career:	
Wage	$_____ / year $_____ / hour
Preparation	
Number of job openings in _____	
Number of new job openings in the next 10 years	

E **PROBLEM-SOLVE.** Why is it important to look for a high-demand job that matches your skills and interests?

_____

_____

_____

_____

Lesson 4: Reading

A DEVELOP YOUR ACADEMIC SKILLS. Read the Academic Skill. Answer the questions.

1. Preview the title and image in Exercise B. What do you think the main idea of the text will be?
   a. a man who wanted to build a new school in Ghana
   b. a man who wanted to run for president of Ghana
   c. a man who wanted to build a new hospital in Ghana

2. Skim the article. Find an example signal word or phrase. Write it below.

_____

B ▶ READ. Listen and read.

Giving Students in Ghana a New Beginning

1   What kind of change would you make in your community? Would you open a new school? A new hospital? A new park? Patrick Awuah wanted to change education in his country. He set goals for himself, and he achieved them. In so doing, he touched the lives of thousands
5   of people across Africa.

Awuah had an impressive career trajectory. He grew up in Accra, the capital of Ghana. In 1986, he moved to the United States. He attended Swarthmore College on a full scholarship. After graduating, he worked for Microsoft for several years. In 1997, Awuah left Microsoft to enroll in business school. He earned his business degree at the
10 University of California.

Awuah dreamed of opening a university back home in Ghana. At that time, there were only a few universities in Ghana, which was not enough for a country of nearly 20 million people. While in business school, Awuah worked on a business plan to build a university. He and a team traveled to Ghana. They did a study on how to open a university there.

15 Awuah graduated from business school in 1999. He moved back to Ghana that same year. In 2002, he opened Ashesi University. *Ashesi* means "beginning" in Fante, a Ghanaian language. Awuah saw the university as a beginning point for future leaders. He wanted Ashesi graduates to transform Africa. Since the university opened, thousands of graduates have done just that. They have opened banks. They have launched information technology companies. They have built manufacturing plants. Others have helped

20 build infrastructure. For instance, several Ashesi alumni work at Google and General Electric. These
companies have invested billions of dollars in Africa's infrastructure.

In 2017, Ashesi won the World Innovation Summit for Education prize. It is a very prestigious prize. Only
six schools win each year. Awuah has received much acclaim for his work, too. For example, the president
of Ghana awarded him the Order of the Volta in 2007. This is an honor awarded to people for outstanding
25 service to the country. In 2015, Awuah won the MacArthur Fellowship award. This award is given to just a
few people each year. It celebrates people who change the world in innovative ways. In 2015, he was also
named as one of the world's 50 greatest leaders by *Fortune* magazine.

Awuah has demonstrated through his life that the way to achieve your dreams is to have a plan. Ashesi
University's graduates are a testament to this strategy.

C **LOCATE DETAILS.** Read the article again. Then read the statements and decide if they are true or false.
Write the line numbers of your evidence.

	T/F	Lines
1. In the 1990s, there were 40 million people in Ghana.	_____	_____
2. *Fante* means "beginning" in a Ghanaian language.	_____	_____
3. Thousands of Ashesi graduates have opened businesses across Africa.	_____	_____
4. In 2017, Patrick Awuah won the MacArthur Fellowship award.	_____	_____

D **ANALYZE.** Read the article again. Answer the questions.

1. Reread the first paragraph. What is the main idea?
   a. Patrick Awuah thinks everyone should make a difference in their community.
   b. Patrick Awuah dreamed of changing education in his country.
   c. There are many ways to make a difference in your community.

2. Reread the second paragraph. What is the main idea?
   a. Awuah had an impressive career.
   b. Awuah was born in Accra, Ghana.
   c. Awuah went to business school.

3. Reread the third paragraph. What is the main idea?
   a. In the 1990s, Ghana only had a few universities.
   b. Awuah dreamed of opening a university in Ghana.
   c. In the 1990s, there were almost 20 million people living in Ghana.

4. Reread the fourth paragraph. What is the main idea?
   a. Ashesi graduates have opened businesses across the continent.
   b. *Ashesi* means "beginning" in Fante, a Ghanaian language.
   c. Awuah hoped Ashesi University graduates would transform Africa.

5. Reread the fifth paragraph. What is the main idea?
   a. Ashesi University and Patrick Awuah have gotten a lot of praise.
   b. The MacArthur Fellowship award is a very prestigious prize.
   c. In 2017, Ashesi won the World Innovation Summit for Education prize.

Lessons 5 & 6: Grammar

A IDENTIFY. Read the paragraph. Underline the gerunds. Circle the infinitives.

Alan began working as a server at a chain restaurant because he needed to earn some money. Initially, he didn't have any interest in the restaurant business. However, after a few years of doing the job, he began to dream about becoming a regional manager. Once a month, a regional manager came by to talk to Alan's boss and the employees. It was the regional manager's job to oversee all the restaurants in an area and make sure everyone was happy. Alan liked the idea of traveling and talking to people, but he wasn't sure about the requirements to get a job like that. After three years as a server, he decided it was time to start working toward his goal. Getting more information was the first item on his list, so Alan decided to ask his manager for a meeting to discuss his plans.

B MODIFY. Complete the sentences. Use a gerund or an infinitive form of the verb in parentheses.

1. _____ a business is one of my long-term goals.
   (own)
2. Sometimes I have difficulty _____ specific short-term goals.
   (set)
3. It's important _____ skills that will be in demand in the future.
   (acquire)
4. One of the best ways _____ success is to set realistic goals.
   (achieve)
5. The counselor advised me _____ a realistic time frame for my goals.
   (establish)
6. I will continue _____ my goals as circumstances change.
   (revise)
7. I've thought about _____ with an academic advisor, but I haven't done it yet.
   (consult)
8. It would be interesting _____ an assessment and find out if my goals are realistic.
   (take)
9. My plan is _____ my long-term goal within the next 10 years.
   (achieve)
10. This week, I'm meeting with my boss _____ for her advice.
    (ask)

C USE CONTEXT CLUES. Complete the conversation. Use the gerund or infinitive form of the verbs in the box.

apply	ask	become	find out	make
meet	move up	open up	oversee	talk

Alan: Thank you for _____ with me today. I was hoping _____ to you about my goals and my future here at the restaurant.

Manager: Absolutely. What's on your mind?

Alan: Well, I'm interested in _____ how I can work my way up to regional manager.

Manager: That's a great long-term goal, but you might want to shift your focus to becoming a restaurant manager first. Regional managers are in upper management. They have a lot of experience _____ restaurants.

Alan: That makes sense. What is the process for _____ a manager?

Manager: Do you have a college degree?

Alan: No. I have a high school diploma.

Manager: Well, I like the initiative you've demonstrated by _____ me for this meeting. We have an assistant manager position _____ soon, and I encourage you _____ for that. However, _____ to manager requires a degree in business. I suggest _____ an appointment with a college counselor.

Alan: Thanks for your help. I'll do that.

D FIND. Read the paragraph. There are six mistakes. The first one is corrected. Find five more and correct them. Write in the corrections where relevant.

What are your long-term goals? Maybe you want to get a position in upper management or apply for a small business loan so you can start your own business. Maybe you just want to acquire a new skill.
Whatever it is, not ~~to set~~ *setting* a time frame for a goal is a common mistake. People often plan on get around to something eventually, but without deadlines, it's hard to stick to those plans. Consider put your goals on a calendar so you can keep track of them. If you often have trouble to meet your deadlines, it may be that you are not setting realistic time frames. Be particularly careful with goals that need being coordinated. Challenge yourself, but don't expect accomplishing the impossible!

E WRITE. Answer the questions with complete sentences. Use gerunds and infinitives.

1. What is one goal you plan to achieve this year?

   _____

2. What part of meeting your goal will be difficult?

   _____

3. What actions will help you meet your goal?

   _____

Lesson 7: Reading

A **DEVELOP YOUR ACADEMIC SKILLS. Read the Academic Reading Skill. Answer the questions.**

1. Preview the title and graph in Exercise B. What do you think the main idea of the text will be?
   a. a lawyer who helps businesspeople in Pittsburgh
   b. a doctor who helps homeless people in Pittsburgh
   c. a doctor in Pittsburgh who is homeless

2. Skim the article. Find an example signal word or phrase. Write it below.

_____

B ▶ **READ. Listen and read.**

Jim Withers: The Hero Caring for Pittsburgh's Homeless

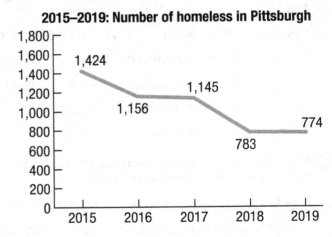

2015–2019: Number of homeless in Pittsburgh

1   For many years, Dr. Jim Withers has had an unusual evening routine. He dresses in simple clothes. He puts dirt on his face. He messes up his hair. Then he walks around Pittsburgh searching for 5 homeless people. He looks under bridges, along the river, and in abandoned buildings. When he finds homeless camps, he introduces himself and asks if he can come in. He tries to make them comfortable. His goal is to give them basic medical care for free.

10   Dr. Withers is often shocked by how sick the homeless people are. For instance, a lot of them have problems from living outside in the cold and the rain. They have frozen fingers and feet. They have burns from trying to keep warm by building fires. Dr. Withers also sees common health problems, such as high blood pressure, diabetes, and asthma. He travels with a backpack full of donated medicines that he gives away to people.

15   In the 1990s, Dr. Withers founded an organization focused on getting homeless people healthcare. The organization takes care of people on the street and at free drop-in clinics. The organization also owns a van. Doctors drive around Pittsburgh providing free medical care to people who live on the streets. After he launched his organization, Mercy Hospital in Pittsburgh began to oversee it. The hospital provides funding and support to Dr. Withers and his team.

20   Dr. Withers's mission has reached doctors and patients around the world. Since Dr. Withers began working in the streets, his team has given free healthcare to over 10,000 people. More than 30 cities

around the world have launched similar programs. Dr. Withers also started a conference for doctors who care for homeless people. More than 1,000 doctors participate in the conference each year. They learn how to bring medical care to the streets in their cities.

25   Dr. Withers often brings medical students to visit homeless camps with him. He calls the visits a "classroom of the streets." He wants the students to see that it doesn't matter where you treat people. The most important thing is to take care of them. Many of the medical students say their visits with Dr. Withers changed their lives. He helped them understand medicine is about helping sick people wherever you find them.

Although his methods are simple and unglamorous, Dr. Withers has touched the lives of many people.
30 He is the perfect example of what it means to be an everyday hero.

C **IDENTIFY. Answer the questions.**

1. Reread the first paragraph. What is the main idea?
   a. Dr. Withers has a different evening routine than most doctors.
   b. Dr. Withers looks for homeless people so he can give them medical care.
   c. Dr. Withers changes his appearance so he can blend in at homeless camps.

2. Reread the second paragraph. What is the main idea?
   a. Many of the people Dr. Withers sees have serious health issues.
   b. Dr. Withers gives away free medicine when he can.
   c. A lot of homeless people have common health problems.

3. Reread the third paragraph. What is the main idea?
   a. Dr. Withers founded an organization that gives homeless people healthcare.
   b. Dr. Withers's organization opened free drop-in clinics.
   c. Mercy Hospital helps fund Dr. Withers's organization.

4. Reread the fourth paragraph. What is the main idea?
   a. Dr. Withers's organization has given free healthcare to more than 10,000 people.
   b. Dr. Withers's mission has had an impact on doctors and patients worldwide.
   c. More than 30 cities around the world have developed similar programs.

5. Reread the fifth paragraph. What is the main idea?
   a. Dr. Withers wants medical students to know it doesn't matter where they treat patients.
   b. Medical students who work with Dr. Withers say he changed their lives.
   c. Dr. Withers often brings medical students on his visits to homeless camps.

D **INTERPRET. Look at the graph in Exercise B. Answer the questions.**

1. How many people in Pittsburgh were homeless in 2016? _____

2. What was the change in the homeless population in Pittsburgh between 2017 and 2019?

   _____

3. In what year was the homeless population in Pittsburgh the highest? _____

4. In what year was the homeless population in Pittsburgh the lowest? _____

Lessons 8 & 9: Writing

Academic Writing Skill: Reinforce topic sentences with supporting details
A topic sentence should be general enough that you can write an entire paragraph about it. Reinforce your topic sentence with narrower supporting details. Good supporting details include examples.

You can use numbers to illustrate your examples. Numbers make your writing more specific and interesting to your audience.

A **STUDY THE MODEL.** Read about Erica's friend.

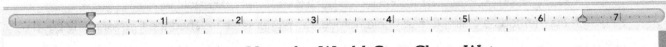

Changing How the World Gets Clean Water

One of the most successful people I know is my friend Guillermo. Guillermo works at the World Health Organization. He and his team help people around the world get clean water. I never knew unsafe drinking water was such a big problem until I learned about Guillermo's job.

Did you know that more than 3,000,000 people die every year from drinking unsafe water? The most common reason is that they get water-borne diseases. Children are particularly vulnerable. Dirty water kills 5,000 children a day. More than 30% of the world lacks access to clean drinking water. Experts say this problem is only going to get worse as the population grows.

Guillermo and his team help bring clean water to people. They build water pipelines to rural areas. They construct centers to clean wastewater. They put filters in water systems. They use inexpensive but effective techniques, like giving away millions of bleach pills. People use the pills to purify their drinking water. Guillermo is making a big difference in the world.

Erica Vasco

B **IDENTIFY.** Reread the writing model. Write the topic sentences.

1. _____
2. _____
3. _____

C **FIND DETAILS.** Reread the writing model. Find examples that use numbers. Write the sentences.

1. _____
2. _____
3. _____

D ORGANIZE. Think about someone successful you know. What do they do? Why do you admire them? Make a list.

- _____
  _____

- _____
  _____

- _____
  _____

- _____
  _____

- _____
  _____

E WRITE. Answer the question "Who is someone successful you know?" Follow the writing model. Add supporting details and examples. Use numbers to make your writing more specific.

F REVISE. Use the Writing Checklist to evaluate your writing and make revisions.

G COLLABORATE. Share your writing with a partner. Use any feedback to improve your writing.

H PUBLISH. Create a final document to share with others.

Writing Checklist	
	The text includes...
Structure:	✓ Paragraphs with examples
Organization:	✓ Topic sentences with supporting details
Word Choice:	✓ Academic words
	✓ Example signal words
Writing Skill:	✓ Effective topic sentences
Grammar:	✓ Gerunds and infinitives that describe someone successful you know

Lesson 10: Workplace Soft Skills

A **DEFINE. Complete the sentence.**

Demonstrating a willingness to learn means that you _____.
- **a.** like to learn new things
- **b.** show others you want to learn new things
- **c.** ask how to do your job

B **EVALUATE. Read Situation 1 and the job applicant's response. Then answer the question.**

Situation 1
You are a new employee at a bakery. You do not
do any baking yourself, but you prepare the baking
ingredients for the master baker. It is a fast-paced work
environment, but you understand your job well. You are
interested in learning more about baking, but when you
ask the master baker questions about baking, he
gets frustrated.

What is your most likely response to this situation?
What is your least likely response?

Response	Most Likely to Do	Least Likely to Do
1. Continue to ask questions when you want to know something.	☐	☑
2. Stop asking questions when you want to know something.	☐	☐
3. Pay attention to what the master baker is doing and learn from his example.	☑	☐
4. Only ask questions when the master baker is on break.	☐	☐

The applicant's response is effective because it recognizes _____.
- **a.** that the master baker is not responsible to teach you baking, but you can learn by example
- **b.** that asking questions demonstrates your willingness to learn
- **c.** that the master baker would like to answer questions during his break
- **d.** the importance of having others help you advance your own career

C **ASSESS. How does the applicant demonstrate a willingness to learn?**

_____

_____

_____

_____

_____

_____

Occupation Profile: Baker

Bakers often work early mornings, late evenings, weekends, and holidays. Many bakers learn with on-the-
job training in bakeries and restaurants. Some also receive training through apprenticeship programs, or
they attend technical or culinary schools.

D **ANALYZE. Read Situation 2 and respond to the situation. Then answer the question.**

Situation 2

You just got hired at a convenience store. Your primary duties include stocking shelves, cleaning floors, and cleaning the bathrooms. When you were hired, the manager mentioned that she may need you to fill in as a cashier from time to time. You had wanted a cashier position in the first place, but that job was not available when you applied. You decide to show your manager that you are a good fit for a cashier position as soon as one opens up.

What is your most likely response to this situation? What is your least likely response?

Response	Most Likely to Do	Least Likely to Do
1. Ask the manager to train you as a cashier because that's the position you really want.	☐	☐
2. Suggest that you can fill in as cashier when other cashiers need breaks.	☐	☐
3. Spend time with the cashiers to watch what they do.	☐	☐
4. Complete all your tasks efficiently and then volunteer to help out at the register.	☐	☐

My response is effective because it recognizes that _____.
  a. cashiers need to take breaks sometimes
  b. the manager should know the position I really want is a cashier position
  c. I need to do a good job in my current position before I earn a new position
  d. I am motivated to be a cashier

E **APPLY. Describe a situation in which you have demonstrated or would demonstrate a willingness to learn in the workplace.**

_____

_____

_____

_____

_____

_____

_____

_____

_____

Occupation Profile: Cashier

Cashiers are usually trained on the job in all kinds of stores. Because of advancements in technology, such as online sales and self-service checkout stands, there will probably be less need for cashiers in the future.

2 Getting a Job

Lessons 1 & 2: Grammar

A **IDENTIFY. Choose the best word to complete the sentence.**

1. You really _____ to do some research on the company before you go to the interview. That way, you can ask relevant questions.

   a. should   **b.** might   **c.** ought   **d.** maybe

2. You _____ want to look up some reviews of the company to see what other people have said about working there.

   a. ought to   **b.** shouldn't   **c.** may   **d.** could

3. You _____ definitely arrange for a mock interview with a friend so you can practice answering questions out loud.

   a. perhaps   **b.** might   **c.** shouldn't   **d.** should

4. You _____ go into the interview unprepared. Ultimately, preparation will make the difference between a good interview and a bad one.

   a. could   **b.** shouldn't   **c.** maybe   **d.** ought to

5. Perhaps you _____ bring a copy of your résumé to the interview in case they ask for it.

   a. should   **b.** may   **c.** might   **d.** shouldn't

6. You _____ visit the interview location in advance so you're sure of the route.

   a. shouldn't   **b.** maybe   **c.** ought   **d.** could

B **COMPLETE. Complete the paragraph. Use the verbs in the box and a modal (*should/shouldn't*, *ought to*, *could*, *may*, or *might*). More than one answer may be possible.**

be	consider	have	make sure	print	want to use

Before you apply for a job online, you _____ that you have gathered all the information you need, such as the addresses and phone numbers of your former employers. You also _____ a template to build a résumé in advance. Many job-search sites allow you to upload a résumé, and using a template can help you build one that looks professional. However, you _____ making small changes to your résumé for each job you apply to. This way, important words from the job ad are clearly featured. Most résumés are filtered through computer programs before a human ever reads them, so your résumé _____ any missing information, or it might be rejected immediately. It _____ a good idea to ask someone to read over and comment on your résumé and application before you send it. If you don't have anyone at home who can do this, you _____ the completed application and have someone check it on paper.

C COMPLETE. Finish the conversation. Use the verbs in parentheses and a variety of modals to offer a polite suggestion.

Emily: I'm thinking about doing some volunteer work, but I don't know where to start.

Amir: Well, you _____ about what kind of work you want to do.
(think)

Emily: I was thinking that I'd like to work outdoors. I want to do something to help the environment.

Amir: In that case, you _____ the parks department. They use a lot of volunteers.
(contact)

Emily: Oh, good idea! Do you know what the time commitment is like?

Amir: It depends on the job. If you're too busy for a regular commitment, you _____ them
(ask)
if they have special events where you could volunteer.

Emily: Yeah, that would be good for me. My schedule changes a lot.

Amir: You definitely _____ any commitments you can't keep! That wouldn't help your
(make)
résumé at all.

Emily: No, of course not. Can you think of anyone else I should call besides the parks department?

Amir: You _____ an online search for "outdoor volunteer jobs."
(do)

D WRITE. Write sentences to give advice about job references. Use the modals in parentheses and information from the box.

Job References
You should ask: your most recent employer, a co-worker you know well, a teacher
You should *not* ask: friends and family, someone you don't know, employers who weren't happy with your work
Remember:
- Don't list people as references without asking them first.
- When you approach people to ask for a reference, show them your résumé and tell them about the job you want.
- It's OK to make suggestions if you want people to mention specific skills you have.

1. (*should*)

_____

2. (*might want to*)

_____

3. (*shouldn't*)

_____

4. (*may not want to*)

_____

5. (*ought to*)

_____

6. (*may want to*)

_____

Lesson 3: Workplace, Life, and Community Skills

A **READ.** Why should you research a company before applying for a job?

Researching Your Dream Company

1   Have you found a job opening at your dream company? Are you already imagining yourself working

there? Before you apply, don't forget to do some research on the company. Start by doing these five things:

1. Visit the company's website.

- Read about the company's mission, vision,

5   and values.

- Learn about the company's leaders.

- Learn more about the specific job you want.

2. Look up recent news about the company online. Is it

growing? Has it made any major changes?

10 **3. Learn more about what the company does.** Make sure you understand what the company

does. What are their products or services? Who are their clients?

4. Research different jobs at the company. What are the most common job titles at the company?

What skills do they require? What is the salary range for different jobs? What benefits does the

company offer?

15 **5. Ask other people in the industry about the company.** Think about people you know who work

in the same industry as the company. Ask them what they've heard. Are the people who work

there happy? Do people often get promoted?

What you find out during your research will help you write a strong cover letter and résumé. You

can show that you are already well informed about the company. You can highlight your professional

20 experiences that are most in line with what the company does. Do all this and you will make yourself a

dream candidate for your dream company.

B **LOCATE DETAILS.** Read the article again. Then read the statements and decide if they are true or false. Write the line numbers of your evidence.

		T/F	Lines
1.	You should research a company after you apply for a job.	___	___
2.	An example of recent news about a company is whether it recently made major changes.	___	___
3.	When you research jobs at the company, you should look up the salary range for different jobs.	___	___
4.	You should wait for your interview to mention what you have learned about a company.	___	___

C **INTERPRET. Read about the company. Choose the correct answers.**

BrightSky Airlines

Home | Book a Flight | Check In | Blog | About Us

Mission, Vision, Values ▶
Leadership
What's New
Careers

MISSION At BrightSky Airlines, our mission is to help our passengers get where they need to go safely and quickly. We are also committed to giving our employees a secure and supportive work environment.

VISION To create a global community of dedicated BrightSky travelers

VALUES diversity, innovation, customer service, respect

1. "Create a group of people around the world who are loyal to the airline." This is an example of the company's _____.
   a. mission   **b.** vision   **c.** values

2. "Give employees a supportive work environment." This is an example of the company's _____.
   a. mission   **b.** vision   **c.** values

3. "Provide good customer service." This is an example of the company's _____.
   a. mission   **b.** vision   **c.** values

D **GO ONLINE. Think about a company that interests you. Find and look at its website.**

1. Find the company's mission, vision, and values. Write them down.
   • Mission: _____
   • Vision: _____
   • Values: _____

2. What do you like about the company's mission and vision? Why?
   _____

3. Look up recent news about the company. What information did you find?
   _____

E **PROBLEM-SOLVE. Why is it important to find a job with a mission, vision, and values that matter to you?**

_____
_____
_____
_____
_____
_____
_____

Lesson 4: Reading

A **DEVELOP YOUR ACADEMIC SKILLS.** Read the Academic Skill. Answer the questions.

1. Preview the title and image in Exercise B. What do you think the main idea of the text will be?
   a. how to prepare for questions at your next job interview
   b. why it's important to improve your technology skills
   c. how you can take certain job skills to any job

2. Skim the article. Find a summary signal word. Write it below.

_____

B ▶ **READ.** Listen and read.

Skills You Can Take Anywhere

1 Do you want to change careers? Do you want to move into a different industry altogether? Maybe you worry that you don't have the right skills. However, you might be more ready than you realize. When you're

5 job hunting, it's important to identify your transferable skills. A transferable skill is one you can use anywhere, regardless of the industry or job. Most employers are seeking people with the same transferable skills. Let's take a look at a few examples:

10 • **Communication:** Employers want employees who can communicate well. They want people with strong verbal and listening skills. Good writing skills are also important. With so much work taking place over email, it's essential that employees be able to express themselves well in writing.

• **Time management:** An employee who can manage his or her time well is very valuable. Employees with strong time management skills are organized. They establish priorities for their work each day.

15 They make and complete their to-do lists on time.

• **Teamwork:** It is important for any employee to work professionally with others. This means being respectful to colleagues and working efficiently with others to achieve a common goal.

• **Technology:** Even if you're not working in a technology field, it's essential to have strong technology skills. In general, employers are looking for people who are comfortable with basic computer programs.

20 They want employees to be open to learning new kinds of software and other tools.

- **Leadership:** Good leaders are dependable. They are responsible. They work hard. They effectively lead a group by making it clear what everyone needs to do and how to prioritize tasks.

You probably already excel at one or more of these skills. However, you can never hone your transferable skills too much. The good news is that you can build transferable skills both at and outside

25 of work. For example, let's say you want to enhance your technology skills, yet you rarely use computers at your job. Volunteering could be a great way to develop your computer skills. Offer to help a nonprofit organization install new software, or learn how to build a website and then build one for free for a community group.

What are your transferable skills? What are some examples of times you've used them in current and

30 past jobs? Overall, talking fluently about your transferable skills will help you stand out in your next job interview.

C LOCATE DETAILS. Read the article again. Then read the statements and decide if they are true or false. Write the line numbers of your evidence.

	T/F	Lines
1. A transferable skill is one that is specific to your industry.	_____	_____
2. An example of teamwork is being respectful to your colleagues.	_____	_____
3. Technology skills are only useful if you work in a technology field.	_____	_____
4. One way to hone your transferable skills is through volunteer work.	_____	_____

D RECOGNIZE STRUCTURE. Think about one of your transferable skills. Then use the STAR technique to describe a time you used that skill. Complete the chart.

STAR Technique Transferable skill: _____	
Situation	
Task	
Action	
Result	

Lessons 5 & 6: Grammar

A **REWRITE.** Rewrite the sentences. Use the present perfect continuous.

1. Jim has worked at a bank since 2016.

   _____

2. Hassan and Mia have studied English for three years.

   _____

3. Some employees have not behaved appropriately.

   _____

4. Victoria and Koji have obviously tried to improve lately.

   _____

5. Jason's illness has affected his performance.

   _____

B **COMPLETE.** Write new sentences from the information provided. Use the present perfect or the present perfect continuous. Add *since* when necessary.

1. I started looking for work in November. I'm still looking for work.

   _____

2. Ben learned new computer skills for his job. Now he's hoping for higher compensation.

   _____

3. Kamila started studying Spanish in 2018. She is still studying it.

   _____

4. Jenni took a computer class in the fall. Now she is taking a different computer class.

   _____

5. Ms. Perez and Mr. Lee interviewed four people for the job. They just finished the interviews.

   _____

6. Roberto practiced for his job interview. Now he feels confident and ready.

   _____

C IDENTIFY. Read the paragraphs. Circle the verb forms that correctly complete the sentences.

Dress for Success® is a company that gives professional clothes to women who do not have enough money to buy them. Where does Dress for Success get its clothing? Volunteers and clothing companies **have donated / have been donating** clothes to the organization in the past. Dress for Success doesn't just help women dress appropriately for work. The company **has also started / has also been starting** a career center. Since it started, women **have learned / have been learning** computer skills to help them search for jobs.

Nancy Lubin started Dress for Success in 1996 in the United States. It **has grown / has been growing** ever since then. In fact, it **has expanded / has been expanding** to 24 other countries. The company **has helped / has been helping** more than 925,000 women so far. In addition to the regular staff, thousands of volunteers **have worked / have been working** at Dress for Success over the years. More than 14,000 people **have donated / have been donating** time in just the last year!

D USE CONTEXT CLUES. Complete the paragraph. Use the present perfect or present perfect continuous form of the verbs in the box.

decide	interview	look	show up	take	tap

What makes a great job interview? We asked Tony Flores, who _____ more than 150 employees as the manager of Acme Warehouse.

"Obviously, a lot of factors affect my decision. I want employees who have the appropriate skills and experience, but the interview itself also makes a difference. The first thing I notice is if the candidate _____ the time to dress appropriately. You'd be amazed at how many people _____ for interviews in wrinkled or stained clothes! I'm also always looking for someone who can make eye contact. If I notice that a candidate _____ at his or her hands or the floor throughout an interview, I take it as a sign that the person lacks confidence—or even that he or she is dishonest! Other aspects of a candidate's body language influence my decision. I _____ not to hire more than one person because they weren't sitting up straight!"

Lesson 7: Reading

A **DEVELOP YOUR ACADEMIC SKILLS. Read the Academic Reading Skill. Answer the questions.**

1. Preview the title and graph in Exercise B. What do you think the main idea of the text will be?

   _____

2. Skim the article. Find a summary signal word or phrase. Write it below.

   _____

B ▶ **READ. Listen and read.**

How Do We Prepare for the Jobs of the Future?

1   What will jobs be like 50 or 100 years from now? We probably don't even have names for many of

the jobs that will exist then! Imagine trying to describe a software developer or web architect to a farmer

from 100 years ago. What we do know is that many of the jobs in tomorrow's world will require strong

technology skills and soft skills. Soft skills are personal traits that allow someone to interact effectively with

5   others. People with exceptional technology skills and soft skills will have an upper hand in the job market

of the future.

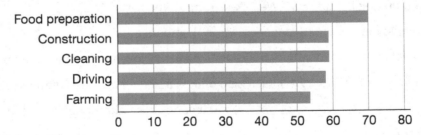

Percentage of Jobs at Risk of Being Automated in the Next 50 Years

One of the reasons so many jobs will require technology skills is that millions of jobs will be automated

over the next 50 years. This means computers or robots will do the jobs instead of humans. The jobs

most likely to be automated are in the food service, construction, cleaning, driving, and farming industries.

10 Robots will increasingly prepare our meals, construct our buildings, clean our houses, drive our trucks, and

plant our food. The good news is that there will be job openings for people who can oversee and manage

those robots.

What technology skills do you have right now? Are you good with computers? Can you type quickly?

Can you use different kinds of software? Do you know how to code? If the answer to any of those

15 questions is *no*, consider taking a computer class online or at school.

In tomorrow's job market, another area of focus will be on soft skills. Humans are typically better at soft skills than robots are. For example, people have strong social and emotional intelligence. They are creative and empathetic. They are good at developing complex strategies. These skills are all uniquely human. Soft skills allow people to manage and lead teams more effectively than a robot could.

20 If you're concerned your job might get outsourced to a computer or robot one day, take a look at your soft skills. What are your strongest soft skills? How could you develop them further? Could you take on new tasks at work? Could you do volunteer work?

To sum up, developing your technology skills and soft skills now is the surest way to prepare yourself for tomorrow's jobs. You might even enjoy the added perk of becoming more qualified in your current job. 25 Who knows? Your new skills could even lead to a promotion or pay raise!

C **SUMMARIZE.** Write a brief summary of the article in your own words.

_____

_____

_____

_____

D **CITE EVIDENCE.** Read the article again. Complete the sentences. Write the line numbers of your evidence.

Lines

1. In the next 50 years, _____.
   a. many jobs will be automated across a variety of industries
   b. soft skills will become less important in the workplace
   c. people won't need technology skills because computers will do everything
   _____

2. An example of a soft skill is _____.
   a. typing quickly
   b. social and emotional intelligence
   c. using different kinds of software
   _____

3. Humans will probably always be better than robots at _____.
   a. managing and leading teams
   b. preparing meals
   c. cleaning houses
   _____

E **INTERPRET.** Look at the graph in Exercise B. Then read the statements and decide if they are true or false.

T/F

1. The industry that will be most affected by automation is driving.
   _____

2. More than 60% of food preparation jobs are going to be automated.
   _____

3. Fewer than 50% of construction jobs are going to be automated.
   _____

Lessons 8 & 9: Writing

Academic Writing Skill: Write a résumé tailored to a specific job
A résumé is a list of your skills and job experiences. It is a way for you to introduce yourself to an employer when you apply for a job. It's important to make your résumé specific to the job you are applying for. Employers write job descriptions for a reason—they want to know that you can do a specific job. They want to see evidence in your résumé that you can get to work right away. Before you introduce yourself in your résumé, read the job description carefully. Then use language from the job description in your résumé.

A **STUDY THE MODEL.** Read the job ad and résumé excerpts.

Job: Aircraft Mechanic

Responsibilities:
- replace parts
- repair damaged parts
- diagnose problems with aircraft, make suggestions for how to fix them
- keep reports on all the work you do
- inspect electronics

Carla Frost
9082 Green Street
Los Angeles, CA 90005
(213) 555-1279
cfrost@ymail.com

BrightSky Airlines, Airline Mechanic   October 2017–present
- Perform daily checks to replace or repair parts as needed.
- Work with manager to diagnose and fix problems.
- Keep reports on all maintenance performed.
- Inspect the electronic board daily.
- Train other technicians on new software.

B **FIND DETAILS.** Reread the writing model. Find language in the résumé that matches the responsibilities in the job ad. Write examples.

Job Ad	Résumé
• _____	• _____
• _____	• _____
• _____	• _____

C **ORGANIZE.** Go online to find a job posting that matches your experience, skills, and interests. Then list your qualifications for the job.

- _____
- _____
- _____
- _____

D APPLY. Imagine you are applying for this job. Write an effective introduction to a cover letter. Remember to include a hook.

_____

_____

_____

_____

E WRITE. Begin writing a résumé tailored to this job. Look at the writing model for ideas.

Name: _____

Address: _____

Phone number: _____

Email address: _____

Company and job title: _____   Dates of job: _____

Relevant duties and responsibilities at job:

- _____

- _____

- _____

- _____

F REVISE. Use the Writing Checklist to evaluate your writing and make revisions.

G COLLABORATE. Share your writing with a partner. Use any feedback to make your résumé even more tailored to the job.

H PUBLISH. Create a final document to share with others.

Writing Checklist	
	The text includes...
Structure:	✓ Résumé and cover letter
Organization:	✓ Introduction with a hook
	✓ Body of letter and final conclusion
Word Choice:	✓ Academic words
	✓ Summary signal words
Writing Skill:	✓ Introduction with a hook
Grammar:	✓ Modals to express possibilities
	✓ Present perfect and present perfect continuous

Lesson 10: Workplace Soft Skills

A DEFINE. Complete the sentence.

Projecting self-confidence means that you _____.
    a. believe you are a good employee
    b. think you can learn to do a job well
    c. are comfortable with and can demonstrate your strengths

B EVALUATE. Read Situation 1 and the job applicant's response. Then answer the question.

Situation 1

You are a sales associate at a large sporting goods store. You normally work in the clothing section, but the manager asked you to cover the camping equipment area for two weeks. You don't have any experience with camping, so you don't know the answers to many of the customers' questions.

How would you respond to this situation? Rank the responses below from most to least appropriate. (1 is most appropriate; 4 is least appropriate.) Assign a different rank to each response.

Response	1	2	3	4
1. Answer customers' questions when you can. When you can't, apologize for your lack of experience.	☐	☑	☐	☐
2. Ask the manager to get someone else to cover the camping section.	☐	☐	☑	☐
3. Tell the manager that you know a lot about camping. Answer customers' questions with your best guesses.	☐	☐	☐	☑
4. When you don't know an answer, help customers find the information online or ask a more knowledgeable employee.	☑	☐	☐	☐

The applicant's response is effective because it recognizes that _____.
    a. it's important to project self-confidence by answering all questions, even if you aren't sure your answers are correct
    b. you can show self-confidence by not admitting when a task is difficult for you
    c. being self-confident means you are willing to take on challenges but not afraid to show weaknesses
    d. it's not a good idea to accept responsibilities that will damage your self-confidence

C ASSESS. How does the applicant project self-confidence?

_____

_____

_____

Occupation Profile: Sporting goods sales associate

Sales associates help customers find products in a store. Demand for retail sales associates is expected to decline about 2% in the next decade because of online competition. However, sporting goods is a billion-dollar industry in the United States and is expected to grow.

D ANALYZE. Read Situation 2 and respond to the situation. Then answer the question.

Situation 2

You work as an office assistant. Most of the time, you deal with paperwork. However, when the receptionist is out, you must answer the phone and deal with customers' complaints. You are shy and this is difficult for you.

How would you respond to this situation? Rank the responses below from most to least appropriate. (1 is most appropriate; 4 is least appropriate.) Assign a different rank to each response.

Response	1	2	3	4
1. Apologize to customers and tell them you'll have the receptionist return their call.	☐	☐	☐	☐
2. Learn different ways to respond to customers' complaints and then practice until you become more confident.	☐	☐	☐	☐
3. Deal with customers' complaints as well as you can, even though it makes you uncomfortable.	☐	☐	☐	☐
4. Let the phone calls go to voicemail so the receptionist can deal with customers' complaints when she returns.	☐	☐	☐	☐

My response is effective because it recognizes that _____.
  a. dealing with customers' complaints is part of the receptionist's job
  b. shy people aren't good at dealing with customers' complaints
  c. it's possible to build self-confidence through learning and practice
  d. it's important to apologize to customers when they are unhappy

E APPLY. Describe a situation in which you have projected or would project self-confidence in the workplace.

_____

_____

_____

_____

_____

_____

_____

_____

Occupation Profile: Office assistant

Office assistants file records, type documents, and answer phones. They work in almost every industry, especially schools, healthcare facilities, and government offices. Office assistants usually have a high school diploma.

The Thoughtful Consumer

Lessons 1 & 2: Grammar

A **COMPLETE. Complete the sentences to compare two things. Use *more* or ø.**

1. Money management is _____ easier than it seems if you stay on top of it.

2. If you are going over budget a lot, you may need to do a _____ better job of anticipating your expenses.

3. If you are within your budget but aren't saving any money, you may need to make a _____ restrictive budget.

4. If your monthly income is irregular, it may be _____ difficult to keep to your budget.

5. Keep in mind that in some months you will have _____ bigger expenses than in others.

6. If you have a lot of fluctuating expenses, you should create a _____ flexible budget.

B **MODIFY. Complete the paragraphs. Use the comparative forms of the words in the box.**

accurate	carefully	cheap	expensive
few	good	hard	modern

Karen's apartment had a lot of problems and was very old, so she wanted to move to a place that

was _____. She found a great apartment with a brand-new kitchen, but of course it was

_____ than her old apartment. She decided that she could afford it if she kept track of her

spending _____. Karen moved into the new apartment and created a budget.

The first month, she found that it was _____ to stick to her budget than she had expected.

She realized that she needed to eat out _____ times per week, and she couldn't keep buying

things at the corner market. She found a _____ grocery store a few blocks away, and that

helped her save some money. At the end of the month, she made a few adjustments to her budget so the

next month's numbers would be _____. After a few months of trial and error, Karen was finally

in control of her finances, and she felt much _____ about her living situation.

C COMPARE. Read the information about two different credit cards. Use the words in parentheses to make comparisons.

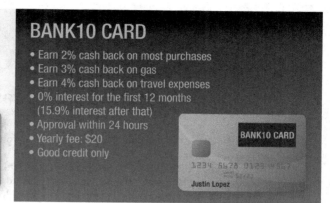

Red Card

- Earn 1.5% cash back on most purchases
- Earn 2% cash back on travel expenses
- 0% interest for the first 6 months
  (23.5% interest after that)
- Immediate approval
- Yearly fee: $50
- Bad credit OK!

BANK10 CARD

- Earn 2% cash back on most purchases
- Earn 3% cash back on gas
- Earn 4% cash back on travel expenses
- 0% interest for the first 12 months
  (15.9% interest after that)
- Approval within 24 hours
- Yearly fee: $20
- Good credit only

1. (high interest rate)

    _____

2. (generous cash-back program)

    _____

3. (approved fast)

    _____

4. (good credit to apply)

    _____

5. (long zero-interest period)

    _____

6. (low yearly fee)

    _____

D FIND. Correct the mistake in each sentence.

1. Everyone wants to make a more high salary.

2. Sometimes getting a raise doesn't seem to make you any more rich.

3. Many people find that when they make more money, they just spend it more quick.

4. For most people, housing is a more big expense than anything else.

5. Eliminating some of your entertainment expenses can be painful, but spending too much money now will be painfuller in the future.

6. You will feel more bad in the long run if you end up in debt.

7. You can cut back on your grocery bill more easier if you cook most of your meals at home.

8. You have to decide which expenses are importanter than others.

9. Speaking to a financial consultant is a more better idea than trying to figure out your finances by yourself.

10. The spending cutbacks were difficult, but we're more happy with our savings account now.

Lesson 3: Workplace, Life, and Community Skills

A **READ.** Why is it important to save money?

Moneywise

Home | Resources | Blog | About Us

Five Tips to Start Saving Today

1   Saving money is a lot like budgeting. In both cases, it helps to have a plan and set goals. If you follow these five tips, you should start seeing your savings grow in no time!
    Add a savings goal to your budget. It's never too late to
5 start saving. Figure out how much money you can afford to save each month. It's important to have at least a few hundred dollars set aside in case of emergencies. For example, you might need to fix a kitchen appliance, or you might have an unexpected medical bill. No amount of money is too small. Think about this:
10 If you save $50 a month every month, you'll have saved $3,000 after five years!
    Monitor your spending. Pay close attention to your expenses each month. How much do you spend on things you don't really need? Next month, try cutting out small
15 unnecessary purchases. Bring coffee to work in a reusable container. Ride a bike to work instead of taking the bus. Put that money in savings. Once this becomes a habit, you'll be amazed at how quickly you can save money every day.
    Identify your goal and track your progress. If you are saving for something big like a house or car, it's important to track your progress. As you see your savings grow, you will be even more motivated to keep saving.
    Save for your retirement. Ask your employer about retirement benefits. Many companies will match the amount
20 of money you put into a retirement account.
    Save for your children's education. If you have children, it's never too early to start saving for college. Most banks offer special savings accounts for education expenses. Talk to your bank and find out what you need to do to open an education savings account.

B **LOCATE DETAILS. Read the article again. Then read the statements and decide if they are true or false. Write the line numbers of your evidence.**

	T/F	Lines
1. If you save $50 a month, you'll have $3,000 saved after three years.	____	____
2. If you are saving money for a big purchase, tracking your progress will motivate you.	____	____
3. It is rare for an employer to match the amount of money you put into a retirement account.	____	____
4. Your bank might offer special savings accounts for your children's education.	____	____

C INTERPRET. Read the chart. Choose the correct answers.

An interest rate represents how much money a bank will give you if you open a savings account with them. For example, your bank offers a 1% interest rate on savings accounts. If you put $100 in savings, your bank will give you $1.

These three people opened savings account this month. Read about their interest rates.

	Money in Savings Account	Monthly Interest Rate	Interest Earned	Total
Maria	$1,000	1.5%	$15	$1,015
Ben	$2,000	1%	$20	$2,020
Hana	$500	1.25%	$6.25	$506.25

1. Who has the highest interest rate? _____
2. Who has the most money in their savings account? _____
3. Who earned the most interest? _____
4. Who earned the least interest? _____

D GO ONLINE. Find a local bank's website. Look at the information about savings accounts.

1. What is the name of the bank?

_____

2. What do you need to do to open a savings account?

_____

3. What is the interest rate for a savings account?

_____

E PROBLEM-SOLVE. Why is it a good idea to get into the habit of saving money each month?

_____

_____

_____

_____

_____

_____

_____

_____

_____

_____

Lesson 4: Reading

A **DEVELOP YOUR ACADEMIC SKILLS. Read the Academic Skill. Answer the questions.**

1. Preview the title and image in Exercise B. What do you think the main idea of the text will be?
   a. alternatives to buying a brand-new phone
   b. the average price of a new phone
   c. features you should look for in a new phone

2. Skim the article. Find a word or phrase that compares or contrasts. Write it below.

_____

B ▶ **READ. Listen and read.**

Do you really need a brand-new phone?

1   These days, we often feel inseparable from our
smartphones. They give us directions, check our email,
and allow us to keep up with social media and the
news. However, smartphones are also delicate and can

5 break easily. If your phone breaks and your warranty is
expired, it can feel daunting to think about replacing it
with an expensive brand-new phone. Fortunately, you
have options. You could consider buying a refurbished
or used phone.

10   A refurbished phone is similar to a new phone. In fact, even the newest models are often available as
refurbished phones. Phone companies and phone repair shops buy used phones from people. Then they
refurbish them. This means they inspect, update, and repair the phones before they sell them. Refurbished
phones often look as good as new. However, they may not come with the original accessories. They are
usually protected by a warranty. The typical warranty lasts for a year. Refurbished phones are almost

15 always cheaper than new phones.

    By contrast, a used phone is one you buy directly from someone who doesn't want it anymore. Like a
refurbished phone, a used phone should be cheaper than a new phone. Unlike refurbished phones, there
is no guarantee the phone is in good shape. If there is something wrong with a used phone, you may not
have any way to replace it. The phone probably won't have a warranty. If it breaks, the person who sold

20 it to you may not want to give you your money back. The phone may or may not come with the

original accessories.

In addition to cost savings, there are environmental benefits to buying a refurbished or used phone. Many people get a new cell phone every few years, but few think about what happens to their old phones. Only 20% of phones are recycled. That means most of the other 80% wind up in landfills. This is

25 problematic because cell phone batteries contain toxic chemicals. These chemicals leak into the soil, water, and air. By purchasing a refurbished or used phone, you keep one fewer phone from going into a landfill.

The next time you need a new phone, think about your options. Keep refurbished and used phones in mind. You could save a lot of money and do some good for the environment in the process.

C **CITE EVIDENCE. Read the article again. Complete the sentences. Where is the information? Write the line numbers.**

Lines

1. A refurbished phone is _____.
   a. a phone you buy from someone who doesn't want it
   b. a used phone that has been updated and repaired
   c. a brand-new phone you buy from the phone company

   _____

2. Refurbished phones _____ come with a warranty.
   a. almost never
   b. don't
   c. usually

   _____

3. _____ a refurbished phone, if a used phone breaks, it can be hard to get your money back.
   a. Unlike
   b. Similar to
   c. Like

   _____

D **BRAINSTORM. Imagine you need a new laptop computer. You could buy a new, refurbished, or used laptop. What would you do before making the purchase? Why?**

1. Before buying a new laptop, I would _____.

2. Before buying a refurbished laptop, I would _____.

3. Before buying a used laptop, I would _____.

Lessons 5 & 6: Grammar

A COMPLETE. Complete the sentences with the superlative form.

1. We bought our car from the dealership on 10th Street because they offered us _____ trade-in deal.
   a. better　　　　　**b.** the good　　　　　**c.** the best　　　　　**d.** best

2. He has several big debts, but he's paying the short-term car loan off _____.
   a. the fastest　　　**b.** fastest　　　　　**c.** the most fast　　　**d.** the faster

3. If you buy the _____ used vehicle you can find, it will inevitably have problems.
   a. cheapest　　　　**b.** cheaper　　　　　**c.** more cheap　　　　**d.** most cheap

4. We're looking for a long-term loan with the _____ interest rate possible.
   a. low　　　　　　**b.** lowest　　　　　　**c.** most low　　　　　**d.** lower

5. Which of these cars goes the _____ on a tank of gas?
   a. far　　　　　　**b.** farther　　　　　　**c.** farthest　　　　　**d.** most far

6. I chose this lease because it had the _____ terms.
   a. reasonable　　　**b.** too reasonable　　**c.** best reasonable　　**d.** most reasonable

B USE CONTEXT CLUES. Complete the conversation with adjectives from the box. Use superlative forms.

affordable	bad	convincing	embarrassing
expensive	good	low	pretty

Hiro: Wish me luck! I'm off to buy a used car.

Sonia: Really? I'll never buy a used car again. I had _____ experience the last time I did that.

Hiro: What happened?

Sonia: Well, it's partly my fault. I was looking through the ads online and _____ car I saw was this red one with a really nice paint job.

Hiro: Uh-oh. And you didn't get it inspected before you bought it?

Sonia: Nope. I feel so dumb. It's one of _____ things I've ever done. The car looked great and seemed like _____ deal I could get. I wanted to take it to my mechanic, but the guy said he had another buyer and didn't want to wait.

Hiro: And you believed him?

Sonia: I did! He had _____ way of speaking. Somehow, I felt like my only option was to hand over the cash.

Hiro: Oh no! And then what happened?

Sonia: The car broke down almost immediately, and my mechanic said it would cost more than $1,000 to fix. That was _____ price he could offer, and he's _____ mechanic in town!

Hiro: Wow. What did you do?

Sonia: I just sold it for parts. The guy I bought it from disappeared, and I wasn't going to put more money into a junk car. I lost a lot of money. It was _____ mistake I've ever made.

Hiro: Ouch. Well, I'm still going to look at this car, but I'll be sure to get it inspected before I buy it!

C **FIND. Read the paragraph. There are six mistakes. The first one is corrected. Find five more and correct them. Write in the corrections where relevant.**

One of ~~the~~ best financial decisions I made last year was to buy a bike instead of a car. Rather than spending all my money for a down payment on the cheaper car I could find, I bought a very nice bike. The bike doesn't just save me money—it also saves me time! I compared the times for driving, taking the train, and riding my bike to work. Believe it or not, during rush hour, riding my bike is the faster! I feel good about riding my bike to work because pollution from cars is one of the most bad things about this city, and it contributes to climate change. Finally, riding a bike almost every day has been great exercise. I'm the healthy I've ever been. Getting a bike wasn't just a great financial decision, it was one of the more smartest decisions I've ever made!

D **COMPARE. Read the information about three different cars. Use the superlative forms of the words in parentheses to make comparisons.**

Sedan
3 years old
56,000 miles
24 miles per gallon
$13,000
30-day warranty

Hybrid
2 years old
31,741 miles
54 miles per gallon
$20,000
100-day warranty
Buy now, get $1,200 rebate!

Compact
Brand New!
30 miles per gallon
$23,500
60-month warranty
Lots of options
Buy now, get $1,000 cash rebate!
Low interest rate and leasing options available!

1. (old) _____
2. (expensive) _____
3. (long warranty) _____
4. (high mileage) _____
5. (cheap) _____
6. (fuel efficient) _____

E **WRITE. Write sentences about purchases you have made. Use the superlative forms of the adjectives in parentheses.**

1. (good) _____
2. (expensive) _____
3. (smart) _____
4. (big) _____

Lesson 7: Reading

A DEVELOP YOUR ACADEMIC SKILLS. Read the Academic Reading Skill. Answer the questions.

1. Preview the title and infographic in Exercise B. What is the purpose of the article? What information do you expect to read about? _____

2. Skim the article. What two things does the article compare and contrast?

   _____

B ▶ READ. Listen and read.

Working for Yourself vs. Someone Else

1   Have you ever wondered what it would be like to own your own business? Many people fantasize about being their own boss. They imagine they'd be able to do whatever they want, whenever they want. Even though that may be true, running a small business can be risky and a lot of work.

    Whether you have your own business or work

5 for someone else, many of the basics are the same. You have a salary and benefits. You have a specific role in the company. In both situations, you typically work with colleagues and customers.

    However, that is where most of the similarities

10 end. Starting a small business is usually very stressful and time consuming. Many small business owners work day and night. They work on weekends, and they work on holidays. Despite doing

WHAT IS A SMALL BUSINESS? 500
A small business is a company with fewer than 500 employees.

There are
30 million
small businesses
in the United States.

Approximately **50%** of all small business owners work from home.

59 million people work for small businesses.

what they love, they often struggle to find a work-life balance. In the beginning, many small business owners

15 manage all the tasks at their company. They help customers. They manage money. They build the website. They oversee staff members and create policies. A big risk for small business owners is burnout. When small business owners work too hard for too long, they get so exhausted they have a hard time working.

    Cash flow is a big stressor for small businesses. It can also contribute to burnout. Cash flow is the total amount of money coming in and going out of a business. When you start a small business, the single most

20 important thing is to find customers. Without customers who pay you money, your business won't last

long! Nevertheless, many small businesses have a hard time finding customers. Even when they do, their customers sometimes take a long time to pay them. A whopping 82% of small businesses fail because of cash flow problems.

By contrast, when you work for someone else, you have a lot less responsibility. You don't have to
25 worry about cash flow. You don't have to work around the clock. You get paid regularly, and you have job security. If you don't like what you're doing, you can always find a new job.

Starting your own business could be a good move if you think you can find customers easily and don't mind working long hours. However, if you prefer a set schedule and less stress, you are probably better off working for someone else.

C CITE EVIDENCE. Read the article again. Complete the sentences. Where is the information? Write the line numbers.

                                                                                      Lines

1. Owning a business and working for someone else are similar in that you _____.   _____
   a. get a salary and benefits at both
   b. often need to work evenings, weekends, and holidays
   c. are your own boss

2. An example of a cash flow problem is when _____.   _____
   a. a customer pays a business quickly
   b. a business has too many customers
   c. customers don't pay on time

3. _____ owning a small business, you usually don't have to worry about cash
   flow when you work for someone else.   _____
   a. Similar to
   b. In contrast to
   c. Just like

D INTERPRET. Look at the infographic in Exercise B. Match the numbers with the phrases to complete the sentences.

1. A small business has fewer than _____ employees.   **a.** 59

2. In the United States, _____ million people work for small business owners.   **b.** 500

3. Approximately _____ percent of small business owners work from home.   **c.** 30

4. There are _____ million small businesses in the United States.   **d.** 50

Lessons 8 & 9: Writing

Academic Writing Skill: Use compare-and-contrast signal words to highlight similarities and differences
When you compare two people, places, or things, you show how they are similar. When you contrast them, you show how they are different. Certain signal words let readers know you are comparing or contrasting. Use the words *both, also,* and *similarly* to show similarities. Use the words *unlike, by contrast,* and *however* to show differences. This will clarify your writing and help your readers understand what you are trying to say.

A **STUDY THE MODEL. Read about two different ways you can plan a vacation.**

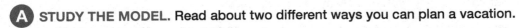

What Is the Best Way to Plan a Vacation?

Many people save money all year to take a vacation. There are two main ways to plan a vacation. The first is to buy an all-inclusive package. The second is to plan the trip yourself.

With both kinds of vacation planning, you must book hotels, flights, and a rental car. You also need to decide where you want to go and what activities you want to do. Similarly, you have to decide if you want to eat in restaurants or cook your own meals.

The biggest advantage of a vacation package is that you pay for everything at once. That includes hotels, flights, a rental car, meals, activities, and even childcare. You don't have to worry about a thing; everything is planned for you. You just need to show up!

By contrast, if you plan your own trip, you have to book everything yourself. This might be appealing if you are a frugal traveler. You can search for cheap flights, travel during off-peak times, or rent an apartment. Unlike hotels, apartments usually have kitchens where you can cook meals to save money. However, this is too much work for some people. They're better off with a vacation package.

No matter who plans your vacation, it is always a treat to take some time off and connect with your loved ones.

B **FIND DETAILS. Reread the writing model. What compare-and-contrast signal words does the writer use?**

_____

C **RESEARCH. Choose two types of vacations. Go online and research their similarities and differences. Choose 3–4 criteria to compare and contrast. Take notes below.**

- road trip
- cruise
- trip to another country
- trip to the beach
- camping trip
- package vacation

D ORGANIZE. Take your notes and organize your ideas in a Venn diagram.

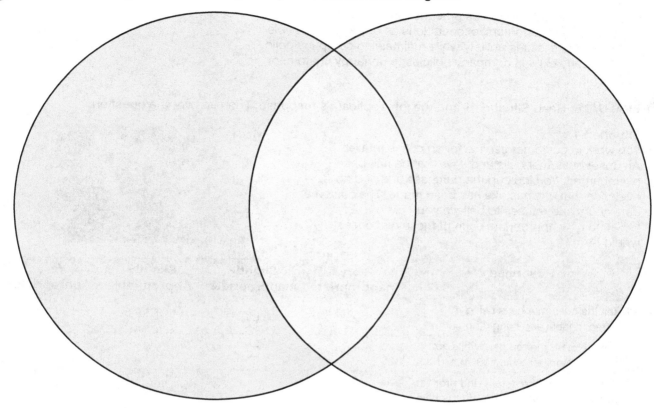

E WRITE. Write a compare-and-contrast essay. An easy way to organize your essay is to discuss all the similarities in one paragraph and all the differences in another. Remember to use compare-and-contrast signal words. Don't forget to include an introduction and a conclusion!

F REVISE. Use the Writing Checklist to evaluate your writing and make revisions.

G COLLABORATE. Share your writing with a partner. Use any feedback to improve your writing.

H PUBLISH. Create a final document to share with others.

Writing Checklist	
	The text includes...
Structure:	✓ Compare-contrast essay
Organization:	✓ Introduction
	✓ Body of essay
	✓ Final conclusion
Word Choice:	✓ Academic words
	✓ Compare-contrast signal words
Writing Skill:	✓ Signal words to highlight similarities and differences
Grammar:	✓ Comparative and superlative adjectives and adverbs

Lesson 10: Workplace Soft Skills

A **DEFINE. Complete the sentence.**

Responding effectively to customer needs means that you _____.
   a. meet all customers' expectations as quickly as possible
   b. address issues politely while maintaining company policy
   c. clearly explain company policies to unhappy customers

B **EVALUATE. Read Situation 1 and the job applicant's response. Then answer the question.**

Situation 1
You work in customer service for an online retailer.
An upset customer calls and says that he has been
overcharged. You look up the purchase and find no
evidence that any mistake has been made. The customer
gets angry and refuses to believe you.
   Rate how appropriate each of these responses
would be.

Response	Very Inappropriate	Slightly Inappropriate	Slightly Appropriate	Very Appropriate
1. Tell the customer he is being unreasonable and hang up on him.	☑	☐	☐	☐
2. Put the customer on hold while you ask the manager what you should do.	☐	☐	☑	☐
3. Write down all the details and promise to call the customer back after you've researched the issue.	☐	☐	☐	☑
4. Transfer the call to someone else who can try to deal with the problem.	☐	☑	☐	☐

The applicant's response is effective because it recognizes that _____.
   a. it's best to have customers talk to someone else if they are angry at you
   b. dealing with angry customers is the manager's responsibility
   c. it's important to reassure the customer while following company policy
   d. there's no point trying to reason with an angry person

C **ASSESS. How does the applicant respond effectively to customer needs?**

_____

_____

_____

_____

_____

Occupation Profile: Customer service representative

Customer service representatives process orders and help customers over the phone. They need to be
good at communicating with people and using computers. Most customer service representatives have a
high school diploma and receive on-the-job training. This occupation is expected to decline 2% in the next
10 years because of automation.

D ANALYZE. Read Situation 2 and respond to the situation. Then answer the question.

Situation 2

You work as a server in a busy restaurant. A customer ordered a meal but now says she doesn't want it, and she doesn't want to pay for it. She wants something different. Restaurant policy does not allow customers to change an order after it is brought to the table unless there is something wrong with it. The customer gets very angry when you explain this policy.

Rate how appropriate each of these responses would be.

Response	Very Inappropriate	Slightly Inappropriate	Slightly Appropriate	Very Appropriate
1. Tell the customer that her anger is misdirected because you don't make restaurant policy.	☐	☐	☐	☐
2. Tell the customer that you're very sorry but you just aren't allowed to change the order.	☐	☐	☐	☐
3. Tell the customer you understand how she feels and you'll see if the manager can make an exception.	☐	☐	☐	☐
4. Tell the customer that she has no right to treat people this way.	☐	☐	☐	☐

My response is effective because it recognizes that _____.
- **a.** customers should treat restaurant employees with respect
- **b.** customers need to understand and follow company policies
- **c.** it's fine to make exceptions to company policy if it will make customers feel better
- **d.** it's important to show sympathy to customers and reassure them that I'll try to help

E APPLY. Describe a situation in which you have responded or would respond effectively to customer needs in the workplace.

_____

_____

_____

_____

_____

_____

Occupation Profile: Restaurant server

Restaurant servers can work almost any time of day, including early mornings, late evenings, and weekends. Many servers work part-time and make most of their wages in tips. No formal education is required for this job.

At Peak Performance

Lessons 1 & 2: Grammar

A COMPLETE. Complete the sentences.

1. _____ I showed a lot of initiative, I didn't get a promotion.
   a. Despite   **b.** Although   **c.** Due to   **d.** So that

2. Kim is going to move up the career ladder quickly _____ she always goes above and beyond.
   a. due to   **b.** despite   **c.** though   **d.** because

3. Ali had to visit the human resources department _____ finalize his paperwork.
   a. in order to   **b.** so that   **c.** due to   **d.** because of

4. Val didn't have much experience, but _____ her hard work and excellent skills, she was eventually promoted.
   a. because   **b.** despite   **c.** due to   **d.** although

5. Fran took some evening classes _____ she could improve her skills.
   a. so that   **b.** because of   **c.** in order to   **d.** due to

6. _____ his excellent computer skills, Mark didn't get promoted because he's not a team player.
   a. Because   **b.** Despite   **c.** Although   **d.** Due to

7. _____ you've been so flexible about the changes, we're giving you a bonus this year.
   a. Because of   **b.** Due to   **c.** Since   **d.** Even though

8. They hired Toni right away _____ her great attitude.
   a. because   **b.** despite   **c.** although   **d.** because of

B IDENTIFY. Choose the correct ending for each sentence.

1. They hired Tom despite _____.
   a. his lack of experience
   b. he didn't have experience

2. They hadn't given Clara a promotion even though _____.
   a. her years at the company
   b. she had worked at the company for years

3. May was successful at her job because of _____.
   a. her willingness to work with a team
   b. she was willing to work with a team

4. Kira was promoted to manager due to _____.
   a. her flexible attitude
   b. she had a flexible attitude

5. I chose Paul as a mentor because _____.
   a. his excellent communication skills
   b. he has excellent communication skills

6. Lily is taking leadership training courses so that _____.
   a. preparation for a management position
   b. she can prepare for a management position

COMPLETE. Write complete sentences. Use the words in parentheses. More than one answer is sometimes possible.

1. Ann / need to improve her computer skills / get a job

   (in order to) _____

2. the problem / be complicated / have many dimensions

   (because) _____

3. May / have no experience working with a team / know how to collaborate

   (although) _____

4. Pablo / volunteer for committee work / get experience

   (so that) _____

5. Marta / become team leader / her people skills

   (because of) _____

6. Sam / excellent communication skills / be very shy

   (despite) _____

7. Pia / start the job recently / make a good impression on the boss

   (even though) _____

8. Jim / lose his job / his inflexible attitude

   (due to) _____

D **WRITE. Write a sentence with the same meaning. Use the words in parentheses.**

1. Kara is going to get training so that she can get a promotion.

   (in order to) _____

2. Even though it wasn't very good, I'm going to save my performance evaluation.

   (although) _____

3. Because he has an impressive résumé, Bo has received several job offers.

   (due to) _____

4. Due to being a hard worker, Anya has moved quickly up the career ladder.

   (because) _____

5. Despite her late start on her career, Rosa has advanced very quickly.

   (even though) _____

6. The store is seeking new employees because sales have increased recently.

   (because of) _____

Lesson 3: Workplace, Life, and Community Skills

A **READ.** Why does Camila sign up for an online math course?

Getting an Education Online

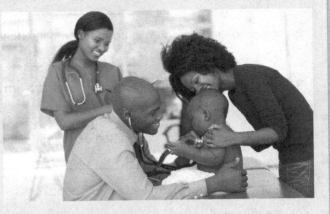

1 Camila is a receptionist at a hospital. After working there for a year, she decides she wants to become a physician's assistant. She asks Mark, a physician's assistant she knows, what next steps

5 she should take. Mark suggests she start by brushing up on her math since he was surprised by how many physician's assistant classes include math.

Camila looks online and finds a free six-week course in math. The course seems straightforward.

10 She needs to watch three videos a week, do two hours of homework, and take a quiz each Friday. Even though the class is free, it is taught by professors at a well-known university. The videos are interesting and engaging. Camila is surprised to find that the coursework is quite manageable.

Camila realizes how much she likes taking courses online. She can go at her own pace and do her homework at night after dinner. She likes the experience so much that she also decides to sign up for a

15 free Spanish class. She hopes she can better help the Spanish-speaking patients at the hospital.

After doing some research, Camila decides to enroll in an online physician's assistant program. She can keep working at the hospital and earn money to pay for her tuition. It had never occurred to Camila that she could become a physician's assistant from the comfort of her home. She is thrilled to discover how many education opportunities are available online.

B **LOCATE DETAILS.** Read the article again. Then read the statements and decide if they are true or false. Write the line numbers of your evidence.

		T/F	Lines
1.	Camila signs up for a free eight-week math class.	——	——
2.	Camila needs to do three hours of homework each week.	——	——
3.	Camila takes an online Spanish course so she can talk to Spanish-speaking patients at the hospital.	——	——
4.	After enrolling in the physician's assistant program, Camila will keep working at the hospital.	——	——

C INTERPRET. Read about the online course. Match the words with the phrases to complete the sentences.

Browse > Math > Introduction to Math

Offered by
Bluebird College
1,520 ratings ★★★★★

Enroll for free!
Length: six weeks
Starts: March 1, 2021
Level: Beginner

About This Course
This course will help you prepare for college-level math. You will watch four videos each week. There will be homework for each video. Don't forget to put your assignments in your calendar. The professor does not accept late homework.

1. The course starts on __d__.
2. The course is for __c__.
3. The course is __a__ weeks long.
4. Students watch __b__ videos a week.

a. six
b. four
c. beginners
d. March 1

D GO ONLINE. Find a website that offers free online courses. Choose a course you are interested in taking.

1. What is the website? _How to become a Public Speaker_
2. What is the name of the course? _Speak as a Speaker_
3. When does the course start? _Nov 15, 2021_
4. How long is the course? _3 months_
5. What work do you have to do each week? _1 speech in front of others_

E BRAINSTORM. What are some advantages and disadvantages of taking an online course?

Advantages	Disadvantages
▷ You can take the course from home	▷ You can not talk in person with the teachers.
▷ You don't have to be in a specific city.	▷ You can not practice in front of others as a real speech
▷ You can share experiences with people from all the World	▷ You don't feel real fear
▷ It could be cheaper	▷ You can't practice on a real stage

Lesson 4: Reading

A **DEVELOP YOUR ACADEMIC SKILLS. Read the Academic Skill. Answer the questions.**

1. Preview the title and image in Exercise B. What do you think the main idea of the text will be?
   a. the advantages of working in an office
   b. the advantages of working from home
   c. why more people are self-employed

2. Skim the article. Find an evidence signal word. Write it below.

_____

B ▶ **READ. Listen and read.**

The Benefits of Telecommuting

1   Can you imagine what a 30-second commute would be like? For people who work from home, that's often how long it takes to get to their desks. More employees are embracing this option, and more employers are

5   giving it to them. In fact, a recent study showed more than 4.7 million Americans telecommute, or work from home, at least half the time.

Telecommuters save thousands of dollars a year. They don't have to pay for gas, parking, or public

10   transportation. They don't need nearly as much professional clothing. They eat lunch and take coffee breaks at home. One study suggests that telecommuters save more than $2,000 a year by working from home.

Saving money isn't the only benefit. Telecommuters say it's more relaxing to work from home than in a busy office. In fact, 82% of telecommuters report lower stress levels than their office peers. Studies also show that telecommuters are more productive and take fewer breaks.

15   One downside of telecommuting is that it can get lonely. People who work at home sometimes lack interaction with their colleagues. Employers can address this by making telecommuting more interactive. They can adopt video conferencing technology. This allows employees to see one another during meetings, no matter where they are. Managers can use this software to hold conference calls and other virtual meetings.

20   Employers have a lot to gain from allowing employees to telecommute. First of all, increased productivity is a big asset. According to one poll, two-thirds of managers claim their employees who telecommute work harder than other employees. This is in part because they can avoid interruptions common in an office. For example, they can skip inefficient meetings, and they aren't distracted by talkative co-workers or loud office spaces.

25   In addition, studies indicate that giving employees the option to work from home keeps them loyal. They are less likely to find new jobs. This means companies don't have to spend as much money hiring new employees. Companies also save money by not having to rent or buy as much office space.

      There is one final and surprising advantage of telecommuting. It's better for the environment. The average person spends an hour getting to and from work every day. By staying off the road, telecommuters
30 produce fewer emissions.

      With all these benefits, it seems likely that telecommuting will become increasingly common. More companies should think about how they can offer this option to their employees. It will make them more competitive.

C LOCATE DETAILS. Read the article again. Then read the statements and decide if they are true or false. Write the line numbers of your evidence.

	T/F	Lines
1. Telecommuters can save more than $2,000 a year working from home.	____	____
2. More than 80% of people who work in offices report lower stress levels than telecommuters.	____	____
3. Telecommuters are often distracted by talkative co-workers.	____	____
4. Employees are more likely to stay at a company if they have the option to work from home.	____	____

D BRAINSTORM. This article focuses on the benefits of telecommuting. However, there are also disadvantages to working from home. Think of three reasons why it might be difficult or unpleasant to work from home.

1. _____

2. _____

3. _____

Lessons 5 & 6: Grammar

A COMPLETE. Complete the sentences.

1. My computer isn't working. Would you mind if I _____ yours?
   a. using
   b. not using
   c. used
   d. didn't use

2. I'm sorry, but would you mind _____ personal calls in the office? They're very distracting.
   a. making
   b. not making
   c. made
   d. didn't make

3. It's hard for me to be productive in this noisy room. Would you mind if I _____ downstairs?
   a. going
   b. not going
   c. went
   d. didn't go

4. I'm already familiar with the program. Would you mind if I _____ the orientation meeting?
   a. attending
   b. not attending
   c. attended
   d. didn't attend

5. Mark has been inconsiderate with his co-workers and won't accept any correction. Would you mind _____ him not to be so defensive?
   a. asking
   b. not asking
   c. asked
   d. didn't ask

6. We've been getting ants in the break room. Would you mind _____ dirty dishes in the sink?
   a. leaving
   b. not leaving
   c. left
   d. didn't leave

B REWRITE. Read the sentences. Rewrite them as polite requests using *Would you mind*.

1. Can I sit here?

   _____

2. Turn down your TV.

   _____

3. Don't take my water bottle.

   _____

4. I'm not going to the meeting, OK?

   _____

5. Can I make a personal phone call?

   _____

6. Try to be more consistent.

   _____

7. I'm not going to start the inventory until tomorrow, OK?

   _____

8. Come a few minutes early next time.

   _____

C **FIND.** Read the conversation. There are mistakes with polite requests. The first one has been corrected. Find three more and correct them. Write in the corrections where relevant.

Matt: Hey Emma. Would you mind ~~to help~~ *helping* Frank clean the tables?

Emma: Sure, but I'm pretty busy right now. Would you mind if I do it in about 10 minutes?

Matt: That's fine. Thanks a lot for your cooperation.

Emma: Of course. By the way, would you mind if I'm leaving an hour early next Saturday? My sister is getting married. Carla said she can come in early to cover my shift.

Matt: That's fine, but I need you and Carla to put the change in the scheduling app. It's company policy. Would you mind take care of that tonight?

Emma: Of course. We'll do it right away.

D **WRITE.** Read the situations. Write a polite request using *Would you mind.*

1. Your co-worker often sings while he is working. It's very distracting.

   _____

2. You have to step out of the office for a minute. You want your co-worker to answer your phone while you're out.

   _____

3. Your supervisor said that it's your choice to attend today's meeting, and you'd rather not because you are busy. Your co-worker wants you to come.

   _____

4. You are collecting money for a co-worker's going-away party. You want another co-worker to contribute $3.

   _____

5. You want to borrow a co-worker's chair while she is out for lunch.

   _____

6. Your co-worker is using the copy machine near your desk. It's loud and you are trying to record something on your computer.

   _____

Lesson 7: Reading

A DEVELOP YOUR ACADEMIC SKILLS. Read the Academic Reading Skill. Answer the questions.

1. Preview the title and infographic in Exercise B. What is the purpose of the article? What information do you expect to read about? _____

2. Skim the article. What does Blue Leopard do?

   _____

B ▶ READ. Listen and read.

A Closer Look: Blue Leopard's Sales and Marketing Organizational Chart

1   Blue Leopard is a company that helps other companies design and develop new products. Blue Leopard recently put together an organizational chart of its sales and marketing team. Many companies use organizational charts to show which employees work in a department and what their titles are. Organizational charts are infographics that also show who works for whom.

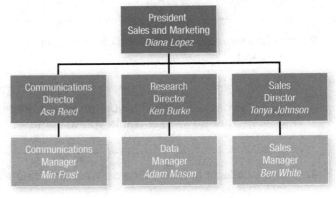

Organizational charts are useful for several reasons. First, they help employees understand the hierarchy at a company. Second, they show what

10   each department does. Within each department, they also show each person's main responsibility. Third, an organizational chart helps people see who they should contact if there is a problem. Let's take a look at Blue Leopard's organizational chart.

Diana Lopez is the president of the sales and marketing department. She is at the top of the

15   organizational chart. Her department has one key task. It needs to attract new customers. Diana oversees how the company will get new customers. Diana manages three people—Asa Reed, Ken Burke, and Tonya Johnson. Asa, Ken, and Tonya execute the company's sales and marketing strategies. They each manage one person.

Asa oversees communications. She makes sure people hear about Blue Leopard. She puts ads for the

20   company in magazines and on the radio. She ensures the company is mentioned in newspaper articles. Asa attends conferences and meets potential customers. Asa manages Min Frost. Min is in charge of social

media for the company. She also writes the company's newsletters. Min helps customers stay informed about what's going on at Blue Leopard.

Ken manages research. He finds out what Blue Leopard's customers need to know. Then he collects
25 data on that topic. He analyzes the data and makes decisions. Ken oversees Adam Mason. Adam's job is to find and pull together the data Ken needs. Sometimes, Adam uses the data to write reports for the company's customers.

Tonya oversees sales. She helps Blue Leopard find new customers. She also keeps existing customers happy. Her job is to understand what customers want and how to keep them. Tonya manages Ben White. Ben
30 keeps track of the thousands of customers in the company database. He keeps their information up to date.

Each employee has a unique job to do, but they all work together to make sure Blue Leopard's sales and marketing department runs as smoothly and efficiently as possible.

C CITE EVIDENCE. Read the article again. Complete the sentences. Where is the information? Write the line numbers.

Lines

1. An organizational chart is an infographic that shows _____.   _____
   a. who reports to whom
   b. employees' names and titles
   c. both a and b

2. Asa's job is to _____.   _____
   a. analyze data for Blue Leopard's customers
   b. make sure people know about the company
   c. manage customers in the company database

3. Ken's job is to _____.   _____
   a. do research for Blue Leopard's customers
   b. find new customers
   c. write the company's newsletters

4. Tonya's job is to _____.   _____
   a. put ads for the company on the radio
   b. help the company find new customers
   c. manage Blue Leopard's social media

D INTERPRET. Look at the organizational chart in Exercise B. Match the names with the phrases to complete the sentences.

1. Min reports to _____.   a. Ben

2. Tonya manages _____.   b. Ken

3. _____ is the Research Director.   c. Asa

4. Ken manages _____.   d. Adam

5. _____ is at the top of the organizational chart.   e. Diana

Lessons 8 & 9: Writing

A STUDY THE MODEL. Read about Wanda's performance review and her employee self-evaluation.

Wanda's Performance Review

Wanda is an assistant director of sales at ABC Software. Every December, the company's managers meet with their employees. During the meeting, they talk about the employee's progress. They discuss the employee's upcoming projects and goals. Often, the managers suggest areas where the employees can improve. These meetings are called performance reviews.

Wanda's performance review is next week. As part of the review, she needs to fill out a self-evaluation and answer several questions about herself. Wanda will share her evaluation with her manager, who will use it for her performance review.

Employee Self-Evaluation

Name: Wanda Charles

Title: Assistant Director of Sales

1. What new responsibilities have you taken on in the past year?

    > I started managing customers in the database. I learned how to create reports with the data. I also helped my manager write the annual marketing and sales plan.

2. What are some of your goals for the next six months?

    > I'd like to get more experience managing people. I'd be happy to help train the new sales manager when that person is hired next year. I'd also like to help build the new website. I have a web design background, and I would like to use those skills at work.

3. What could help you develop more in the next year?

    > I'd like to take a class to develop my management skills. I currently manage two part-time employees. I think I'm a pretty good manager, but I'd like to learn some new strategies.

B FIND DETAILS. Reread Wanda's self-evaluation. Who is her audience? What is her tone?

Audience: _____

Tone: _____

C ORGANIZE. Think about your life at work, school, or home over the last year. What new responsibilities have you taken on? What are your goals for the next six months?

New Responsibilities	Goals
• _____	• _____
• _____	• _____
• _____	• _____
• _____	• _____
• _____	• _____

D WRITE. Answer the self-evaluation questions. Follow the writing model. Remember to use a formal tone.

1. What new responsibilities have you taken on in the past year?

_____

_____

2. What are some of your goals for the next six months?

_____

_____

3. What could help you develop more in the next year?

_____

_____

E REVISE. Use the Writing Checklist to evaluate your writing and make revisions.

F COLLABORATE. Share your writing with a partner. Use any feedback to improve your writing.

G PUBLISH. Create a final document to share with others.

Writing Checklist	
	The text includes...
Structure:	✓ Self-evaluation
Organization:	✓ Responsibilities
	✓ Goals
Word Choice:	✓ Academic words
	✓ Objective language
Writing Skill:	✓ Tone to match audience and purpose
Grammar:	✓ Language to express purpose and reason

Lesson 10: Workplace Soft Skills

A **DEFINE. Complete the sentence.**

Negotiating to resolve a conflict means that you _____.
- **a.** demonstrate the importance of following procedure
- **b.** calmly discuss the pros and cons of a variety of ideas
- **c.** work with someone to find a solution to a problem

B **EVALUATE. Read Situation 1 and the job applicant's response. Then answer the question.**

Situation 1
You work as a clerk at a local supermarket. Your boss asks you and a co-worker to set up a new display and make signs together. You start working on the display, but your co-worker keeps doing other things and not helping you. You're getting very annoyed with him.
   What are the most and least effective ways of dealing with this situation?

Response	Most Effective	Least Effective
1. Ask the manager to intervene and make your co-worker more cooperative.	☐	☐
2. Stop working on the display so your co-worker realizes it won't get done without his help.	☐	☑
3. Make a list of each task that needs to be done and then work with your co-worker to share the tasks.	☑	☐
4. Keep reminding your co-worker that he needs to help you.	☐	☐

The applicant's response is effective because it recognizes that _____.
- **a.** some people need a lot of help to follow through with their responsibilities
- **b.** you should deal with problems directly by coming to an agreement with the other person
- **c.** it's important for management to ensure that employees do their jobs
- **d.** if people are not being cooperative, there is no point in doing their work for them

C **ASSESS. How does the applicant negotiate to resolve a conflict?**

_____

_____

_____

_____

_____

_____

Occupation Profile: Supermarket clerk

Supermarket clerks arrange items on store shelves, remove old items, and bring in new ones. They also help unload and unpack new items that are delivered. This job may involve heavy lifting.

D ANALYZE. Read Situation 2 and respond to the situation. Then answer the question.

Situation 2
You are responsible for billing at a medical clinic, and your work requires a lot of concentration. One of the receptionists who works in the same room is very loud and likes to have long conversations with the patients who call the clinic. You find it hard to concentrate.

What are the most and least effective ways of dealing with this situation?

Response	Most Effective	Least Effective
1. Play loud music on your computer so she notices how distracting it is.	☐	☐
2. Say "Shhh" every time she's too loud so she realizes she is distracting you.	☐	☐
3. Tell your other co-workers about the problem you're having to see if they feel the same way. Ask them to come with you and ask the receptionist to speak more quietly.	☐	☐
4. Compliment your co-worker on her friendliness and then explain the issue. Work with her to come up with a signal you can use to show you're having trouble concentrating.	☐	☐

My response is effective because it recognizes that the best way to negotiate the conflict is to _____.
   a. try to establish a good relationship but also be direct about the problem
   b. clearly explain to the other person why her behavior is disruptive
   c. find others who feel the same way so we can confront the person together
   d. show the other person I am not afraid to confront her about behavior I don't like

E APPLY. Describe a situation in which you have negotiated or would negotiate to resolve conflict in the workplace.

_____

_____

_____

_____

_____

_____

_____

_____

_____

Occupation Profile: Medical billing specialist

Medical billing specialists keep track of patient records and are responsible for collecting payments from insurance companies. They must have knowledge of insurance guidelines and specialized training in accounting. This job usually requires some formal training after high school, such as an associate's degree in healthcare administration. Employment in this area is expected to grow in the next 10 years.

A **IDENTIFY.** Read the paragraph. Underline the adjective clauses. If it's possible to omit the relative pronoun, cross it out.

Homelessness has been increasing for decades, and it is a complicated problem that requires more than one kind of solution. Long-term affordable housing is the first issue that we need to address. Shelters provide protection for people who are sleeping outside, but that is only a temporary solution. Once homeless people are provided with long-term housing, they can access other services that will help them make permanent changes. For example, they can get the healthcare that they need. Long-term housing also gives people the stability that is required for participating in job-training programs. For homeless families, long-term housing often results in children who stay in school and are more connected to their communities. There are many nonprofit organizations whose members are working hard to connect people with affordable housing. Hopefully, their efforts will drastically reduce the number of people who end up living on the streets or in shelters.

B **COMPLETE.** Complete the sentences with the missing relative pronouns.

1. We spoke to the man _____ was evicted from Apartment 18.

2. Sometimes, the temporarily homeless are people _____ lives have suddenly changed.

3. Many homeless people are working, but they are making an income _____ isn't enough to pay for housing.

4. Some cities, such as Seattle, have extremely high rents _____ many people can't afford.

5. They aren't as visible, but there are many homeless people _____ are sleeping on friends' sofas.

6. Many cities build shelters _____ are only a temporary solution to the problem.

7. Often, homeless people cannot simply move to another city _____ is less expensive.

8. Subsidies can help people _____ jobs don't pay enough to cover the rent.

9. The homelessness problem is apparent in many cities _____ have expensive housing.

10. Some people receive a subsidy _____ helps pay for their housing.

C COMPLETE. Complete the conversation between a nonprofit employer and a job applicant. Use the phrases in the box.

I have done	who need it most
that could help them	who needed things like food, clothing, and
that your organization does	school supplies
who had insufficient income to pay	whose families can't provide everything they need
the rent	you were able to help

Tim: Why are you interested in working with us?

Mei: Well, I'm very impressed with the work _____. You help the people in this city _____.

Tim: Do you have any experience working with homeless people?

Mei: No, but in many ways, the job is similar to some volunteer work _____. I volunteered at a preschool in a low-income neighborhood. There were many children _____. They often needed extra support with basic needs.

Tim: What was your role?

Mei: I identified families _____. Then I put them in touch with food banks and other local agencies _____. When I found a family _____, I would contact your organization to help them find affordable housing. That's why I'm familiar with what you do. I knew a couple of families _____.

Tim: Excellent!

D FIND. Each sentence has an error with an adjective clause. Correct the errors.

1. She works for a nonprofit organization that it helps people find affordable housing.

2. There are some government subsidies whom will help you pay your rent.

3. Yesterday, I talked to the neighbors had been evicted from their apartment last year.

4. The organization helps people whom have insufficient income.

5. It may be difficult to understand someone who problems are very different from your own.

6. This house needs a lot of repairs that I don't know how to do them.

E WRITE. Complete the sentences with adjective clauses. Use your own ideas.

1. Homelessness is a problem _____

_____.

2. I think we should help people _____

_____.

3. In most cities, there are shelters _____

_____.

Lesson 3: Workplace, Life, and Community Skills

A **READ.** What is one example of a renter's right?

What Are Your Rights as a Renter?

1   If you are renting your apartment or house, it's important to know your rights. It's also crucial to be familiar with your landlord's rights. That way, if there are any problems, you can figure out who is responsible for handling them.

5   As a renter, you have the right to a property where everything is in good working order. Your doors and windows should lock. Your toilets, sinks, and water heater should work. Your apartment or house may come with air conditioning and heating. If so, it should be easy to adjust the temperature for both. Similarly, appliances such as a refrigerator, stove, or dishwasher should be running well. Many

10   renter laws depend on what state you live in. Check your local laws. For example, you may have rights to additional items, such as smoke detectors or fire extinguishers.

     Your landlord's rights are for you to pay your rent on time and be a good renter. This means you won't damage the property. If you do, you may have to pay for the repairs. Check for damages to the property before you move in. If you find any, take pictures. Show your landlord. This way, you won't

15   be responsible for the repairs. Your landlord has another right that is actually your responsibility. You need to give notice when you plan to move out. Usually, the lease will specify how much time the landlord requires.

     Knowing your rights as a renter will help keep your relationship with your landlord smooth and professional.

B **LOCATE DETAILS.** Read the article again. Then read the statements and decide if they are true or false. Write the line numbers of your evidence.

	T/F	Lines
1. Renters have a right to functioning toilets and sinks.	____	____
2. All renters have rights to fire extinguishers in their property.	____	____
3. You might be responsible for any damage to your apartment.	____	____
4. Landlords have a right to know when you are going to move out.	____	____

C INTERPRET. Read the excerpt of an apartment lease. Answer the questions.

Apartment Lease

Date of lease: 5/14/2021
Renter: Andrew Carras
Apartment: 451 Vidalia Road, Apartment 104

1. RENT: The renter will pay $1,450 on the first day of each month.

2. DEPOSIT: The renter will pay a $2,900 security deposit.

3. NOTICE: The renter will give six months' notice before moving out.

4. UTILITIES: The renter is responsible for paying all utilities.

5. PETS: Pets are not allowed in the apartment.

1. How much is Andrew's monthly rent? _____

2. How much is Andrew's deposit? _____

3. Can Andrew have a dog in his apartment? _____

4. Who is responsible for paying Andrew's utilities? _____

5. If he wants to move, how much notice does Andrew need to give his landlord? _____

D GO ONLINE. Look up the renter's and landlord's rights in your state. Write down any rights that aren't mentioned in Exercise A.

Renter's Rights:

- _____
- _____
- _____

Landlord's Rights:

- _____
- _____
- _____

E PROBLEM-SOLVE. What problems have you encountered as a renter? What did you do? What suggestions do you have for other renters to avoid those problems?

_____
_____
_____
_____
_____
_____

Lesson 4: Reading

A DEVELOP YOUR ACADEMIC SKILLS. Read the Academic Skill. Answer the questions.

1. Preview the title and graph in Exercise B. What do you think the main idea of the text will be?
   a. the reason why rent has gone up over the past few years
   b. the reason why buying a home is getting more expensive
   c. how the 2008 housing crash affected the rental market

2. Skim the article. Find a problem-and-solution signal word or phrase. Write it below.

_____

B ▶ READ. Listen and read.

Why Is Renting So Expensive?

1   Have you noticed how expensive apartments have gotten recently? Rental prices have hit an all-time high over the past few years. In some cities, it's actually cheaper to buy a house than to rent an apartment! To address this issue, we need to first understand what is causing rents to skyrocket. Then we can think about how to lower rental prices to realistic levels.

5   First, let's take a closer look at why rent has gotten so high. One of the biggest issues is that rental costs are rising more quickly than wages. The National Low Income Housing Coalition recently issued a report about high rental prices. The report found that two people working minimum-wage jobs would not be able to afford to rent an average two-bedroom apartment. They would need to earn nearly $23 an

10   hour to afford such an apartment. However, the federal minimum wage is just $7.25 an hour. A general guideline is that you shouldn't spend more than 30% of your income on rent. It would be nearly impossible to

15   meet this target if you were earning minimum wage.

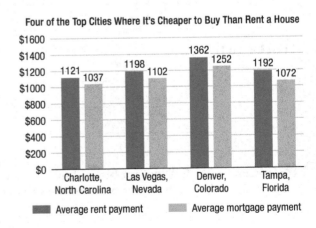

Four of the Top Cities Where It's Cheaper to Buy Than Rent a House

Charlotte, North Carolina: 1121 / 1037
Las Vegas, Nevada: 1198 / 1102
Denver, Colorado: 1362 / 1252
Tampa, Florida: 1192 / 1072

■ Average rent payment   ■ Average mortgage payment

The second issue is that there are more houses for sale than there are available rental units. Millions of houses were foreclosed during the 2008 housing crash. Many of these houses are still on the market. As older people start to retire and downsize, they are selling their houses and moving into apartments. This is putting even more pressure on the rental market.

20   The third issue is also related to the 2008 housing crash. To prevent another crash, mortgage

companies have tightened their lending laws. As a result, some people who want to buy a house can't.

Even though they earn enough money to afford a house, they are locked out of the housing market.

    How should we solve this problem? More than 75% of Americans agree that the best solution is to

adopt rental caps. This would mean landlords could only charge a certain amount of money per unit.

25 Oregon passed a law to cap rent in 2019. Other states, such as California and New York, are planning to

adopt similar laws. Given how many Americans support rental cap laws, politicians in other states should

seriously consider this remedy.

C LOCATE DETAILS. Read the article again. Then read the statements and decide if they are true or false.
Write the line numbers of your evidence.

	T/F	Lines
1. In general, incomes are rising faster than rental costs.	_____	_____
2. The federal minimum wage is $9.25 an hour.	_____	_____
3. Many houses foreclosed during the 2008 housing crash are still for sale.	_____	_____
4. Three-fourths of voters support rental cap laws.	_____	_____

D INTERPRET. Look at the graph in Exercise B. Match the cities with the phrases to complete
the sentences.

1. In _____, it's $120 less expensive to buy a house than to rent.   **a.** Las Vegas

2. In _____, it's $96 more expensive to rent than to buy a house.   **b.** Tampa

3. _____ has the most expensive mortgage payment.   **c.** Charlotte

4. _____ has the least expensive rent payment.   **d.** Denver

E EVALUATE. Use information from the article to complete the graphic organizer.

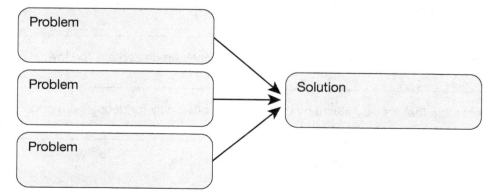

Lessons 5 & 6: Grammar

A COMPLETE. Complete the sentences with adjective clauses from the box. Then rewrite the sentences, reducing the adjective clauses to adjective phrases.

that is being offered this week	that are listed on the website
who are buying the house down the street	that was paid on the loan
that confirm our residency status	that range from very low to very high
that was earned during the last three years	that were rejected by banks

1. What was the total amount of interest _____?

   _____

2. The Smiths have had three loan applications _____.

   _____

3. We had to show them documents _____.

   _____

4. You can find apartments here with rents _____.

   _____

5. We'd like to secure the rate _____.

   _____

6. Did you see the prices _____?

   _____

7. We talked to the people _____.

   _____

8. Please write down your gross income _____.

   _____

B REWRITE. Reduce the adjective clauses to adjective phrases.

1. The loan officer described some problems that are encountered by many people.

   _____

2. People who are applying for loans may not realize that their credit score is too low.

   _____

3. The interest rates that are advertised by the banks are often only for people with good credit.

   _____

4. There are many fees that are associated with buying a house.

   _____

C USE CONTEXT CLUES. Complete the sentences with words in the box. Write the verbs in the correct form.

apply	be	for rent	include
look	pay	take	write

Liz: This website is great for people _____ to buy a new home.

Omar: Really? What's so great about it?

Liz: Well, first of all, it lists pretty much every property _____ sold.

Omar: Nice.

Liz: It also shows all the prices _____ for the house in the past.

Omar: Does it have pictures of the houses?

Liz: Yes. There are lots of photos _____ by professional photographers, so they make the houses look really good. Of course, there are also descriptions _____ by sellers, so you need to be cautious about trusting those. Sometimes, buyers are disappointed when they see a house in person.

Omar: Does it have any information for people _____ for a mortgage?

Liz: In a way. There's no loan information, but you can figure out the sum of your total monthly payment based on the down payment, the price of the house, and current interest rates. Of course, the rates _____ in their calculations are probably the best ones and for people with good credit.

Omar: That makes sense. What if you can't afford to buy? Does it have information about houses _____ in the area?

Liz: Yes, it does.

D REWRITE. Combine the sentences. Change the second sentence to an adjective phrase.

1. There are some low-interest loans. They are available to people with a good credit score.

   _____

2. The loan officer reviewed the documents. The documents were submitted by the applicants.

   _____

3. The bank will offer low-interest rates to people. The people must earn a high income.

   _____

4. Charles was surprised by the amount of the loan. The loan was approved by his bank.

   _____

5. Many homes are still unaffordable for people. The people get paid an average salary.

   _____

Lesson 7: Reading

A DEVELOP YOUR ACADEMIC SKILLS. Read the Academic Reading Skill. Answer the questions.

1. Preview the title and image in Exercise B. What is the purpose of the article? What information do you expect to read about?

   _____

2. Skim the article. What are 3D-printed houses made from?

   _____

B ▶ READ. Listen and read.

Are 3D-Printed Houses the Future of Affordable Housing?

1   Can you imagine living in a house that came out of a printer? For millions of people around the world,

that will be a possibility in the near future. Worldwide, more than 1 billion people currently lack adequate

shelter. Inexpensive 3D-printed houses might be a solution to that problem.

    In 2018, a company called ICON made history. It was the first company in the United States to build

5 a home using a 3D printer. The process is remarkably similar to how a traditional computer printer works.

You send a pattern to the printer. The printer then uses materials to build the object. For a printed house,

the most common materials are cement, sand, metal, and recycled plastic.

    ICON's 3D printer is capable of printing houses

that are anywhere from 500 to 2,000 square feet. The

10 average ICON home has two bedrooms, a kitchen,

a living room, and a bathroom. The houses are

designed to withstand local weather, such as severe

storms, rain, and wind.

    A charity called New Story has partnered with

15 ICON. New Story hopes to solve the housing crisis

in Central America. Tens of millions of people there lack safe shelter. Using ICON's technology, New

Story can print homes quickly. These houses are just a fraction of the cost of traditional houses. ICON's

printer can build one home a day for just $4,000. New Story has already used the printers to build nearly

3,000 homes in Haiti, El Salvador, Bolivia, and Mexico. The charity identifies the families most in need in a

20 community. Then it gives them the houses for free. Each family owns its own house immediately.

ICON hopes more Americans will consider living in 3D-printed houses. It could be an affordable alternative to renting for many people. Printed houses could significantly shake up the U.S. rental market. For the founders of ICON, this is a good thing. They say it is time for a fundamental shift in housing.

Printing homes is sustainable, affordable, and environmentally friendly. The biggest downside is how it
25 could affect the construction industry. Building a 3D-printed house doesn't require many people. Therefore, some construction workers would have to find new jobs. Others would have to learn new skills, such as how to operate computers, printing software, and complicated printers.

That said, the benefits far outweigh the downsides. Countries around the world should start thinking about how they could use 3D printers to provide affordable housing to their citizens.

C LOCATE DETAILS. Read the article again. Then read the statements and decide if they are true or false. Write the line numbers of your evidence.

	T/F	Lines
1. More than 1 million people around the world lack adequate shelter.	_____	_____
2. ICON built the first 3D-printed home in the United States.	_____	_____
3. One of ICON's 3D printers can build one house per day.	_____	_____
4. 3D-printed houses could create a need for more construction workers.	_____	_____

D EVALUATE. Read the article again. Answer the questions to evaluate the author's argument.

1. Problem

   a. What is the problem? _____

   b. What details show the problem is real? _____

   _____

2. Solution

   a. What is the solution? _____

   b. What details support the author's solution? _____

   _____

3. Evaluate the argument.

   a. The problem is a real problem.   Yes / No

   b. The solution is a real solution to the problem.   Yes / No

   c. The reason to support the solution makes sense.   Yes / No

4. What are your thoughts? Do you think the author's solution is a good one? Why or why not?

   _____

   _____

Lessons 8 & 9: Writing

A **STUDY THE MODEL.** Read the conclusion to an article about the rising costs of rent.

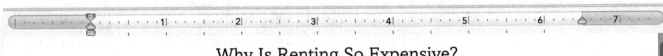

Why Is Renting So Expensive?

How should we solve this problem? More than 75% of Americans agree that the best solution is to adopt rental caps. This would mean landlords could only charge a certain amount of money per unit. Oregon passed a law to cap rent in 2019. Other states, such as California and New York, are planning to adopt similar laws. Given how many Americans support rental cap laws, politicians in other states should seriously consider this remedy.

B **FIND DETAILS.** Reread the writing model. If necessary, reread the entire article on pages 62 and 63. Answer the questions.

1. What is the problem?

   _____

2. What is the writer's solution?

   _____

3. What facts and statistics does the writer use to support the conclusion?

   _____

4. What problem-and-solution signal words or phrases does the writer use?

   _____

C **ASSESS.** Why is this an effective conclusion?

_____

_____

_____

_____

_____

_____

_____

_____

_____

_____

D ORGANIZE. Go online and find a source that describes another possible solution to rising rents. What is the source? What is the solution?

Source: _____

Problem: _____

_____

Solution: _____

_____

_____

_____

_____

E WRITE. Write a problem-solution essay about another solution to rising rents.

F REVISE. Use the Writing Checklist to evaluate your writing and make revisions.

G COLLABORATE. Share your writing with a partner. Use any feedback to improve your writing.

H PUBLISH. Create a final document to share with others.

Writing Checklist	
	The text includes...
Structure:	✓ Problem-solution essay
Organization:	✓ Defined problem and stated solution
	✓ Statistics to provide evidence
	✓ Final conclusion
Word Choice:	✓ Academic words
	✓ Problem-and-solution signal words
Writing Skill:	✓ Clearly stated conclusion
Grammar:	✓ Adjective clauses and phrases

Lesson 10: Workplace Soft Skills

(A) DEFINE. Complete the sentence.

Demonstrating responsibility means that you _____.
- **a.** show you can be trusted
- **b.** do not make mistakes at work
- **c.** do everything your employer asks you to do

(B) EVALUATE. Read Situation 1 and the job applicant's response. Then answer the question.

Situation 1

You are a new employee at a clothing store. It is your co-worker's job to clean the fitting rooms and return clothes to the racks at the end of each day. One day, it's time for you to go home, and you notice she hasn't done this work.

What are you most likely to do in this situation? What are you least likely to do?

Response	Most Likely to Do	Least Likely to Do
1. Leave everything as it is and let someone else deal with it tomorrow.	☐	☑
2. Do the work and mention it to your co-worker the next day.	☑	☐
3. Write a note to the employees working tomorrow and explain that your co-worker didn't do her job.	☐	☐
4. Call the manager and ask what you should do about the situation.	☐	☐

The applicant's response is effective because it recognizes that _____.
- **a.** it's important to make sure a supervisor knows what happened
- **b.** it's normal for people to sometimes forget their responsibilities
- **c.** it's not necessary for you to take on someone else's work
- **d.** the priority is to make sure the work gets done

(C) ASSESS. How does the applicant demonstrate responsibility?

_____

_____

_____

_____

_____

_____

Occupation Profile: Clothing store sales associate

Clothing store sales associates greet and help customers, process payments, and handle returns. They also restock shelves and set up displays. They often work part-time and on weekends. Store employees must be able to stand for long periods of time.

D ANALYZE. Read Situation 2 and respond to the situation. Then answer the question.

Situation 2

You work at a large department store. The store was very busy over a holiday weekend, and now there is a lot of work to be done and not many customers. The manager asked all employees to clean up the store and restock the shelves. However, the manager isn't around, and most of the employees are taking it easy and chatting.

What are you most likely to do in this situation? What are you least likely to do?

Response	Most Likely to Do	Least Likely to Do
1. Take a break and get to know your co-workers. Then make plans to do your tasks the next day.	☐	☐
2. Make sure you do all the work the manager asked you to do.	☐	☐
3. Tell the other employees they are being irresponsible and should get back to work.	☐	☐
4. Call the manager and ask if you can have time to finish the tasks the next day.	☐	☐

My response is effective because it recognizes that _____.
   a. if the supervisor isn't around, I should make sure that all employees do their job
   b. if I don't want to do what is expected of me, I should explain and get permission
   c. good relationships with co-workers are an important part of being successful at work
   d. it's important to show responsibility by completing all tasks assigned to me

E APPLY. Describe a situation in which you have demonstrated or would demonstrate responsibility in the workplace.

_____

_____

_____

_____

_____

_____

_____

_____

_____

_____

Occupation Profile: Retail sales manager

A retail sales manager oversees all store employees and makes sure the store runs smoothly. The manager hires and trains new employees, sets up schedules, and assigns duties to different employees. Most sales managers start working as sales associates before being promoted. Many also have a bachelor's degree in business or communications.

When Nature Is in Charge

Lessons 1 & 2: Grammar

A COMPLETE. Complete the sentences using *if* or *unless*.

1. _____ this storm continues, road conditions will be hazardous in the morning.

2. You won't know what to expect _____ you pay attention to the weather advisories.

3. Highway 12 will be partially flooded _____ it keeps raining like this.

4. We're going to have a difficult winter _____ we are prepared for cold weather.

5. _____ the forecast is really bad, I'll go to the game tomorrow.

6. _____ there are warnings for flash flooding in the canyon, you should leave immediately.

B COMPLETE. Complete the sentences. More than one answer may be possible.

1. If the cold front _____ in before morning, there will be ice on the roads tomorrow.
   a. came   b. will come   c. comes   d. didn't come

2. If he sees a change in the barometer reading, he _____ us know.
   a. is letting   b. will let   c. didn't let   d. lets

3. She won't leave town tomorrow unless the weather _____ nice.
   a. isn't   b. was   c. is   d. can be

4. The storm could damage our home unless we _____ for it.
   a. prepare   b. aren't prepared   c. prepared   d. will prepare

5. If it _____ on Monday, the children won't have to go to school.
   a. snowed   b. will snow   c. snows   d. is snowing

6. There _____ a lot of weather-related accidents if the storm continues through the holiday weekend.
   a. will be   b. can be   c. going to be   d. are being

7. She is always very careful if road conditions _____ hazardous.
   a. will be   b. are   c. were   d. aren't

8. If the storm _____ worse, there will be an advisory.
   a. gets   b. get   c. isn't getting   d. got

9. If the temperature drops below 0, my car _____.
   a. is starting   b. isn't going to start   c. didn't start   d. starts

10. You shouldn't drive anywhere tomorrow unless you really _____ to.
    a. will need   b. need   c. don't need   d. needed

C COMPLETE. Complete the conversation. Use the real conditional of the words in parentheses.

Bill: And now it's time for the weather. Ana, how's the forecast looking for this weekend?

Ana: Not too good, I'm afraid. If you _____ at the radar map, you _____
            (look)   (see)

there's a lot of rain heading our way. And unless this cold front _____ north,
                                                                       (move)

temperatures _____.
              (drop)

Bill: Well, that's bad news for the roads!

Ana: It is. Road conditions will be hazardous, especially at night when it's going to rain the hardest. If you _____ on Saturday night, please _____ home!
(not have to go out) (stay)

Bill: How long can we expect this storm to last?

Ana: Unless something _____, the rain _____ through Tuesday.
(change) (continue)

Bill: I hope you have good news for us after that!

Ana: Well, if you _____ snow is good news, then I _____! We should be
(think) (do)
seeing our first snowfall of the winter later next week.

Bill: Great! If we _____ enough snow, I
(get)
_____ skiing!
(go)

Ana: We probably won't have *that* much snow yet. Unless

something unusual _____, we don't usually
(happen)

_____ enough snow for skiing until December.
(have)

Bill: I know. I'm just hoping!

D **WRITE. Write new sentences about the situations. Use the real conditional.**

1. You are planning to go to the river, but there may be a flash flood advisory.

   _____

2. You have a class tomorrow night, but the roads may be icy.

   _____

3. You want to go to the beach. It's supposed to be sunny and hot next weekend.

   _____

4. Your roof leaks, and there's a rainstorm coming.

   _____

5. You need to go grocery shopping. The forecast says it's going to snow soon.

   _____

6. There's a severe storm coming, and you don't have any food in the house.

   _____

7. The forecast says it will be a beautiful weekend, but sometimes the forecast is wrong.

   _____

8. School may be closed on Monday because of snow. That always makes children happy.

   _____

Lesson 3: Workplace, Life, and Community Skills

A **READ.** What should you include in your emergency kit?

How to Make an Evacuation Plan

1   It's wise to put together an evacuation plan before disaster strikes. That way, you can act quickly and calmly even if there is a sudden crisis like a fire or flood. The most important elements of an evacuation plan are where you will go, how you will get there, and how you will stay in touch with your family members. Once you write your evacuation plan, make sure everyone in your family has a copy.

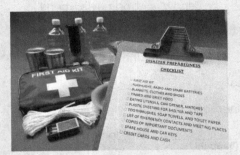

5   When you create your evacuation plan, be sure to include the following information:

Find your local shelter. Look online for a list of emergency shelters in your community. Find the shelter closest to you. Write the address and directions to the shelter in your plan. Include an alternative route in case your planned route is blocked.

Designate an out-of-town meeting place. If you need to evacuate from your town, choose a family
10 member or friend's house where you will go. Write the address and directions to their house in your plan. Map out a route to get to their house. Don't forget to include an alternative route in case your planned route is blocked.

Plan your transportation. How will you get to the shelter or out-of-town meeting place? If you plan to drive, do your best to keep a full tank of gas. You can't know when a disaster will happen. However,
15 sometimes you might have advance notice, like in the case of a storm.

Create a communication plan. Decide how you will communicate. Will one person be in charge of calling everyone else? Will you communicate via text? Write down everyone's phone number in the plan. You should also make an alternative plan for communication in case there is no cell phone service.

20 **Make an emergency preparedness kit.** If possible, you will want to have your emergency kit with you during an evacuation. Make sure your kit includes a radio, cell phone charger, batteries, and medicines.

B LOCATE DETAILS. Read the article again. Then read the statements and decide if they are true or false. Write the line numbers of your evidence.

		T/F	Lines
1.	You should make copies of the evacuation plan for each family member.	_____	_____
2.	Include information about the shelter closest to you in your evacuation plan.	_____	_____
3.	You only need a full tank of gas in case of a storm.	_____	_____
4.	You don't need to include phone numbers in the plan if everyone has a cell phone.	_____	_____

C INTERPRET. Look at the evacuation map. Match the locations with the phrases to complete the sentences.

Pine Street
Oak Lane
4th Avenue
2nd Avenue
3rd Avenue
Main Street
Somerset High School

Evacuation route
Local shelter

1. The evacuation route does not go along _____.   a. local shelter
2. Somerset High School is a _____.   b. Main Street
3. The evacuation route goes along _____.   c. 2nd Avenue

D GO ONLINE. Find the local emergency shelter closest to your home. Write the information below.

Name of the shelter: _____

Address: _____

Directions to the shelter from your home:

_____

E BRAINSTORM. What items specific to you and your family should you include in your emergency preparedness kit?

_____

_____

_____

Lesson 4: Reading

A **DEVELOP YOUR ACADEMIC SKILLS. Read the Academic Skill. Answer the questions.**

1. Preview the title and infographic in Exercise B. What do you think the main idea of the text will be?
   a. places in the world with the most earthquakes
   b. how earthquakes are measured
   c. the biggest earthquakes in history

2. Skim the article. Find a cause-and-effect signal word or phrase. Write it below.

_____

B ▶ **READ. Listen and read.**

The Earthquake Magnitude Scale

1   The top part of our planet is made of layers called tectonic plates. When these plates move or shift suddenly, it is called an earthquake. Earthquakes cause the ground to shake. Consequently, they damage houses, buildings, and streets.

The size of an earthquake is called its magnitude. There are both small and big earthquakes. The

5   earthquake magnitude scale measures their size and strength. This scale goes from 1 to 10.

Earthquakes that measure between 1.0 and 4.9 are small. They are classified as micro, minor, or light earthquakes. If you experience an earthquake of this size, you'll probably feel the ground shake a little. A few objects might fall off shelves. For the most part, there will only be slight damage to houses, buildings,

10   or streets around you. There are millions of small earthquakes around the world each year.

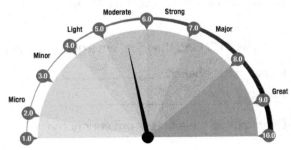

Earthquakes between 5.0 and 6.9 on the scale are bigger. They are classified as moderate or strong. An earthquake of this size will probably damage multiple

15   buildings, cars, and streets. There are more than 1,000 earthquakes of this magnitude each year.

Earthquakes between 7.0 and 7.9 on the scale are severe. They are classified as major. There are fewer than 150 major earthquakes each year.

Any earthquake with a magnitude of 8.0 or more is considered massive. They are classified as great.

20   An earthquake of this size is rare but will likely cause major damage to entire cities and towns. There is

typically only one great earthquake every year or two. The biggest recorded earthquake was in Valdivia, Chile, in 1960. It measured 9.5 on the magnitude scale. It caused landslides and huge waves in the ocean called tsunamis. Some of the tsunamis were more than 80 feet high! As a result of the earthquake, landslides, and tsunamis, thousands of people were killed.

25   Fortunately, a majority of the earthquakes that happen every year are small. However, you don't always know how severe an earthquake is while it's happening. If you ever feel the ground shake—even slightly—you should drop to the floor. Find shelter and hold on. Wait a few minutes after the earthquake is over before you move. Sometimes earthquakes are followed by smaller earthquakes called aftershocks. Most aftershocks happen within an hour of an earthquake. However, they can sometimes continue for as long as
30 a few weeks.

C LOCATE DETAILS. Read the article again. Then read the statements and decide if they are true or false. Write the line numbers of your evidence.

	T/F	Lines
1. An earthquake happens when Earth's tectonic plates move or shift suddenly.	_____	_____
2. There are fewer than 1,000 earthquakes at a magnitude of 1.0–4.9 each year.	_____	_____
3. The biggest recorded earthquake in history was in China in 1960.	_____	_____
4. During an earthquake, you should find shelter and stay there for several minutes.	_____	_____

D INTERPRET. Look at the infographic in Exercise B. Read the article again. Write the possible effects of the different earthquake magnitudes below.

Earthquake Magnitude Scale	Effect(s)
1.0–4.9	
5.0–6.9	
7.0–7.9	
8.0–10.0	

Lessons 5 & 6: Grammar

A COMPLETE. Complete the sentences using verbs in the box.

closed	felt	had	struck
weren't	would assist	wouldn't be	wouldn't take

1. If there were a disaster in this area, FEMA _____ with rescue operations.

2. If we had good plans in place, recovery from these floods _____ so long.

3. We would be stranded here if the roads _____.

4. There would be more tourists here in September if it _____ hurricane season.

5. No one would build brick buildings if we _____ earthquakes in this area.

6. Would our city be prepared if a tornado _____ here?

7. If I _____ an earthquake, I would get under the desk.

8. People _____ so upset with the electric company if we didn't have so many power outages.

B COMPLETE. Complete the conversation. Use the verbs in parentheses to make unreal conditionals.

Parva: What _____ if a hurricane struck this area?
         (happen)

David: Well, that's a scenario I hate to think about! We would have a lot of problems if that

    _____ because we haven't had one for many years. I don't think people are
      (happen)

    prepared.

Parva: We've been having some terrible storms, though. What would happen if the dam

    _____?
     (break)

David: That would be a disaster. If we _____ the dam, the whole valley would flood.
                (lose)

    And if the dam _____ long-term damage, the economic impact on this area
          (suffer)

    would be terrible.

Parva: Do you think it could happen?

David: I suppose it's possible, but the dam is very strong. If we had a really severe storm that lasted a

    long time, I suppose the water _____ over the dam.
                        (go)

Parva: What would that do?

David: It depends on the amount of water. If the water _____ too high, it would flood the
                             (rise)

    houses near the river.

Parva: What about the fish?

David: Well, if we _____ the dam, the fish would be able to swim up the river without any
        (not have)

    problem, so I guess it _____ good for them in the long run. Honestly, if people
               (be)

    _____ back to this area after the flood, they would probably just build a new dam.
     (come)

    We rely on it for our electricity.

C REWRITE. Write the real conditionals as unreal conditionals.

1. If this scenario actually happens, the city is going to be in trouble.

   _____

2. If the storm lasts another week, it will exceed our worst predictions.

   _____

3. If I move to an area with lots of earthquakes, I'll worry about them all the time.

   _____

4. What will you do if there's a hurricane during your vacation on the island?

   _____

5. How will they get back to their homes if the roads are flooded?

   _____

6. If we have another bad tornado here, I'm probably going to move.

   _____

D FIND. Correct the errors to make unreal conditionals. There is one error in each sentence.

1. If this house were in California, we will attach those bookcases to the wall.
2. If there is a hurricane next month, thousands of tourists would be stranded.
3. The insurance isn't so expensive if this weren't a flood-prone area.
4. If we don't have so many big storms in this area, people wouldn't be so prepared.
5. I would keep plenty of emergency supplies in my basement if I live here.
6. Hurricanes would affect this town more if it isn't sheltered by the large bay.

E WRITE. What would you do in these situations? Write sentences using the unreal conditional.

1. A severe snowstorm is predicted for next weekend.

   _____

2. Because of a storm, you are stranded in your home for three days.

   _____

3. You are driving your car and see a tornado in the distance.

   _____

4. Flood water is coming near your home.

   _____

5. Authorities tell you to leave your house to escape flooding.

   _____

6. You have a three-day power outage.

   _____

Lesson 7: Reading

A DEVELOP YOUR ACADEMIC SKILLS. Read the Academic Reading Skill. Answer the questions.

1. Preview the title and map in Exercise B. What is the purpose of the article? What information do you expect to read about?

   _____

2. Skim the article. What is a fault line?

   _____

B ▶ READ. Listen and read.

Why Does Indonesia Have So Many Earthquakes?

1   More than 90% of earthquakes on Earth happen in an area called the "Ring of Fire." This area runs

along the west coast of North America and South America. It extends across the Pacific Ocean to Russia,

Japan, and Indonesia and
down to New Zealand. The
5 Ring of Fire is filled with long
cracks called fault lines. These
cracks are caused when
Earth's tectonic plates move
and smash into one another.
10 Shifting fault lines are the most
common cause of earthquakes.
In addition to fault lines, the
Ring of Fire is home to more

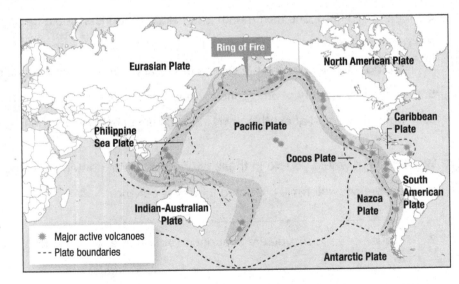

than 450 volcanoes. That's two-thirds of the volcanoes on Earth! Many of these volcanoes are underwater

15 and erupt regularly, causing earthquakes.

Many of the countries along the Ring of Fire experience earthquakes almost continuously. For example,

New Zealand has more than 15,000 earthquakes a year. That's an average of 41 per day! However, nearly

all of these earthquakes are too small to notice. Indonesia, by contrast, suffers 10,000 moderate to major

earthquakes a year. Earthquakes with a magnitude of 5.0 or more happen almost daily in the country.

20   The year 2018 was particularly difficult for Indonesia. There were 11,000 earthquakes. Nine of those earthquakes were a magnitude of 6.0 or greater. The earthquakes affected 2 million people. Tens of thousands of people were killed, and hundreds of thousands of people lost their homes. More than 2,000 people were killed in a single earthquake on the island of Sulawesi.

       Due to its frequent earthquakes, Indonesia is also prone to tsunamis. Tsunamis are enormous ocean
25 waves, and they can be even more dangerous than earthquakes. In 2004, an earthquake in the Indian Ocean caused a tsunami that struck Indonesia. This tsunami killed more than 170,000 people on the island of Sumatra.

       Unfortunately, Indonesia is also prone to other natural disasters. Each year, there are heavy floods during the monsoon season, which runs from November to March. Sometimes, the flooding causes deadly landslides.
30 As if earthquakes, tsunamis, floods, and landslides weren't enough, there are more than 100 active volcanoes in the country. These frequent natural disasters make it hard for Indonesia to keep its infrastructure functioning.

       Indonesia is working hard to improve its disaster response. The country has invested more than a billion dollars in a tsunami early warning system. More than 25,000 schools have launched programs to train students on what to do during an earthquake or tsunami. The government hopes that these measures
35 will save lives in the future.

C **EVALUATE.** Read the article again. Circle the cause-and-effect signal words and phrases. Then underline each cause and put a box around its effect. Draw an arrow to connect each cause to its effect.

D **CITE EVIDENCE.** Read the article again. Complete the sentences. Where is the information? Write the line numbers.

                                                                               Lines

1. The Ring of Fire is _____.   _____
   a. a place in the Pacific Ocean where many earthquakes happen
   b. a place in the Atlantic Ocean where many tsunamis happen
   c. a place where almost no earthquakes happen each year

2. In addition to fault lines, _____ beneath Indonesia frequently cause earthquakes.   _____
   a. tornadoes
   b. volcanoes
   c. big waves

3. Indonesia has more than _____ earthquakes a year.   _____
   a. 100,000
   b. 50,000
   c. 10,000

4. A tsunami is _____.   _____
   a. an island in Indonesia
   b. a long, high wave caused by an earthquake
   c. a crack in the earth where plates shift and smash into each other

Lessons 8 & 9: Writing

Academic Writing Skill: Use complex sentences to create writing that flows
Use complex and compound sentences to help your writing flow. To write a complex sentence, join an independent clause with a dependent clause. To write a compound sentence, join two independent clauses with a conjunction.

Complex Sentence
This allows the foundation to move while the building above stays steady.
(INDEPENDENT CLAUSE)   (DEPENDENT CLAUSE)

Compound Sentence
These buildings kill people when they fall, **and** they cost billions of dollars in damage.
(INDEPENDENT CLAUSE)   (CONJUNCTION)   (INDEPENDENT CLAUSE)

A **STUDY THE MODEL.** Read about earthquake-proof buildings.

Engineering Buildings That Can Survive Earthquakes

Each year, many buildings around the world collapse during earthquakes. These buildings kill people when they fall, and they cost billions of dollars in damage. Engineers are working to develop buildings that can survive earthquakes. Buildings can collapse for many reasons, but the main reason is that they are not built to withstand the side-to-side motion of an earthquake.

The first step to building an earthquake-proof building? Make the building's foundation more flexible. Engineers do this by adding rubber to the cement and steel in the foundation. This allows the foundation to move while the building above stays steady.

The second step is to add shock absorbers beneath the building. You've probably seen or heard about shock absorbers on a car. They are near the wheels, and they help reduce bumpiness when you drive over holes or bumps in the road. Shock absorbers beneath a building act similarly. They absorb vibrations from an earthquake, keeping the building still.

A third step is to build thick rings around the building. The rings are filled with naturally flexible materials, such as bamboo. They catch the vibrations and push them away from the building.

Earthquake-prone cities like Shanghai, San Francisco, and Tokyo are investing billions of dollars in earthquake-proof buildings. Hopefully, the science will develop quickly, and cities will be able to keep up with the demand for buildings that can survive earthquakes.

B **FIND DETAILS.** Reread the writing model. How does the author use complex and compound sentences to create writing that flows? Find one of each type of sentence.

Complex sentence: _____

_____

Compound sentence: _____

_____

C ORGANIZE. Research something people do to survive a severe weather event or reduce damage caused by a natural disaster. What is the process for how it works?

Natural disaster: _____

Solution: _____

_____

Steps in the process:

Step 1: _____

_____

Step 2: _____

_____

Step 3: _____

_____

Relevant details, facts, and examples: _____

_____

_____

D WRITE. Organize your research and put the information in your own words. Follow the writing model. Remember to use signal words to clarify the order of steps. Use complex and compound sentences to make your writing flow.

E REVISE. Use the Writing Checklist to evaluate your writing and make revisions.

F COLLABORATE. Share your writing with a partner. Use any feedback to improve your writing.

G PUBLISH. Create a final document to share with others.

Writing Checklist	
	The text includes...
Structure:	✓ Process essay
Organization:	✓ Introduction with a catchy lead-in
	✓ Body of essay and final conclusion
Word Choice:	✓ Academic words
	✓ Cause-and-effect signal words
	✓ Sequence signal words
Writing Skill:	✓ Complex and compound sentences for writing flow
Grammar:	✓ Real conditionals

Lesson 10: Workplace Soft Skills

A **DEFINE. Complete the sentence.**

Exercising leadership means that you _____.
   a. have an important position, such as a supervisor or manager
   b. complete all tasks your supervisor asks you to do
   c. take charge of a situation so others will follow you

B **EVALUATE. Read Situation 1 and the job applicant's response. Then answer the question.**

Situation 1
You are the assistant manager in a shipping department. It is your responsibility to make sure items are loaded onto trucks smoothly and safely. You have an idea to improve the way this is done. Some of the employees like your idea, but some don't want to change. One of them complains to the manager about your changes.

How would you respond to this situation? Rank the responses from 1 (most effective) to 4 (least effective).

Response	1	2	3	4
1. You decide to abandon your changes to avoid conflict among the employees.	☐	☐	☐	☑
2. You call a meeting, explain what the employee did, and tell everyone why this behavior was inappropriate.	☐	☐	☑	☐
3. You ask to meet with the employee privately and explain that talking to the manager without talking to you first was inappropriate.	☑	☐	☐	☐
4. You ignore the employee's behavior and work hard to demonstrate to the rest of the team that your changes are a good idea.	☐	☑	☐	☐

The applicant's response is effective because it recognizes that a good leader _____.
   a. isn't afraid to reprimand an employee in front of others
   b. confronts inappropriate behavior in a way that won't cause embarrassment
   c. doesn't listen to the opinions of others when they disagree
   d. always tries to avoid conflict in order to maintain a pleasant workplace

C **ASSESS. How does the applicant exercise leadership?**

_____
_____
_____
_____
_____
_____

Occupation Profile: Shipping manager

Shipping managers often work in warehouses or shipping departments of large companies. They pack items for shipment, oversee employees, order supplies, and prepare budgets. They need strong basic math skills and interpersonal skills. In some cases, this job requires an associate's degree in information management or formal training in shipping and receiving.

D ANALYZE. Read Situation 2 and respond to the situation. Then answer the question.

Situation 2

You work in the cafeteria of a large company. Your manager holds a staff meeting once a month so employees can discuss concerns they have. This month, the manager couldn't make it to the meeting. Many of the employees have issues they want to bring up, and they are interrupting one another and going off topic.

How would you respond to this situation? Rank the responses from 1 (most effective) to 4 (least effective).

Response	1	2	3	4
1. Speak loudly so you can get everyone's attention for the issue you want to discuss.	☐	☐	☐	☐
2. Raise your hand and ask everyone to take turns speaking about the issues that concern them.	☐	☐	☐	☐
3. Keep quiet and look at your phone for the rest of the meeting since nothing is getting accomplished anyway.	☐	☐	☐	☐
4. Make an agenda and ask your co-workers to take turns discussing one item at a time.	☐	☐	☐	☐

My response is effective because it recognizes that _____.

    a. it's the manager's responsibility to exercise leadership at the meetings
    b. I can exercise leadership by speaking about my personal concerns at the meeting
    c. I can exercise leadership by making sure everyone is heard in an organized manner
    d. other employees don't need to listen to me because I'm not the leader

E APPLY. Describe a situation in which you have exercised or would exercise leadership in the workplace.

_____

_____

_____

_____

_____

_____

_____

_____

_____

_____

Occupation Profile: Cafeteria worker

Cafeteria workers prepare and serve meals. They also clean kitchen equipment. They need to follow food preparation safety and cleanliness standards. They often work in school, business, or hospital cafeterias. Some cafeteria workers help people in need by working at homeless shelters or soup kitchens.

A COMPLETE. Complete the sentences using words in the box.

as	condition	even	long	only	provided	should	whether

1. We will be able to slow climate change _____ that we start burning less fossil fuel.

2. Consumers need to know _____ or not the packaging on products they buy is biodegradable.

3. _____ we continue to emit greenhouse gases at the current rate, large parts of the planet will become unlivable.

4. _____ long as Antarctic ice continues to melt, sea levels will continue to rise.

5. We can limit methane release from landfill waste _____ if we learn to reuse and recycle more.

6. Climate change policies will only succeed on the _____ that all countries follow them.

7. As _____ as we live in energy-inefficient homes, we will all be contributing to climate change.

8. _____ if we converted all our energy to renewables, that wouldn't be enough to completely stop the planet from warming.

B COMPLETE. Complete the sentences. Choose all possible answers.

1. The future of our planet depends on _____ we respond quickly to the threat of climate change.
   a. whether or not   **b.** if   **c.** provided that   **d.** as long as

2. We can cut emissions _____ we cut back on fossil fuels and take steps to stop deforestation and other problems.
   a. only if   **b.** provided that   **c.** even if   **d.** as long as

3. _____ we plant millions of trees, we still need to cut back on fossil fuel use.
   a. Only if   **b.** Even if   **c.** On the condition   **d.** Whether or not

4. _____ we employ better fishing practices, we may be able to stop overfishing.
   a. If   **b.** Even if   **c.** As long as   **d.** Should

5. Companies should only be awarded contracts _____ they're not going to pollute.
   a. on the condition   **b.** as long as   **c.** should   **d.** whether or not

6. _____ the incidences of natural disasters increases in an area, people don't usually want to leave their homes.
   a. Even if   **b.** If   **c.** Provided that   **d.** On the condition that

7. _____ we allow waste to decompose in landfills instead of recycling it, we'll be contributing to the problem.
   a. Only if   **b.** Whether or not   **c.** Provided that   **d.** As long as

8. _____ we can generate most of our energy from solar, wind, and nuclear sources, we can lower our greenhouse gas emissions.
   a. Only if   **b.** Even if   **c.** If   **d.** Provided that

C REWRITE. Combine the sentences using the connecting words in parentheses.

1. Hopefully, we'll lower our fossil fuel consumption. Otherwise, global warming won't begin to slow down.

   (only if) _____

2. Maybe you can't afford to buy an electric car. There are other things you can do.

   (even if) _____

3. You can limit your greenhouse gas emissions. You just need to put a little effort into it.

   (provided that) _____

4. Maybe individuals will change their behavior, and maybe they won't. Governments and corporations need to address climate change anyway.

   (whether or not) _____

5. Humanity needs to work together to take this problem seriously. That way, we can make the future better for our children.

   (as long as) _____

6. Climate change is attributed to human behavior, so we can slow it down. We just need to change our behavior.

   (on the condition that) _____

D MATCH. Combine the conditions on the left with the ideas on the right. Use the expressions in parentheses.

Conditions	Ideas
• people begin to recycle more	• there will be less waste in landfills
• some areas continue to experience less rainfall	• desertification will increase
• water pollution is cleaned up	• overfishing will still be a problem
• we don't cut down as many trees as we plant	• planting trees will help absorb carbon dioxide
• we do nothing to combat climate change	• the planet may warm as much as 5 degrees by 2100
• people have a garden	• the city has special bins to encourage people to compost

1. (as long as) _____

2. (provided that) _____

3. (even if) _____

4. (on the condition that) _____

5. (should) _____

6. (whether or not) _____

Lesson 3: Workplace, Life, and Community Skills

A **READ.** What is the main purpose of this announcement?

Green Valley Recycling Plant

1   The town of Green Valley recycles paper, plastic, aluminum, and glass. Please put your blue bins by the street every Monday night. We pick up recycling on Tuesday mornings.

    We are pleased to announce you can now recycle many new items at our White Pine location. The location is 259 Pine Street, and it is open Monday–Friday 9 a.m.–5 p.m. Please

5 read the guidelines below about what you can recycle with us.

    Electronics: Do you have old or broken computers, phones, or TVs you no longer use? We work with a company that will take your old electronics and refurbish them. Then they sell them to people who can't afford new electronics. Help us give your old devices a new life.

    Batteries: Did you know you should never throw batteries in the trash? Batteries can break

10 down in a landfill and release dangerous chemicals into the ground. Those chemicals can get into the soil and water. We recycle all kinds of batteries, including car batteries!

    Light bulbs: An estimated 670 million light bulbs go into landfills each year. About half of these light bulbs contain a dangerous chemical called mercury. When the light bulbs break, they release mercury into the landfill and the ground below. When you recycle your

15 light bulbs with us, we will remove the mercury and then recycle the glass.

Thank you for making our recycling program a success!

Sincerely,

The Green Valley Recycling Plant

B **LOCATE DETAILS.** Read the article again. Then read the statements and decide if they are true or false. Write the line numbers of your evidence.

	T/F	Lines
1. You can drop off old batteries at the recycling plant on Saturdays.	____	____
2. The recycling plant works with a company that refurbishes old phones.	____	____
3. The recycling plant accepts any kind of battery except for car batteries.	____	____
4. Light bulbs that aren't recycled can release mercury in landfills.	____	____

C INTERPRET. Read the website. Then match the words with the phrases to complete the sentences.

Recycle Your Old Carpet

Did you know? Your old carpet is filled with complex fibers that don't break down in a landfill. If you want to dispose of an old carpet, don't throw it away. Recycle it! Drop it off at the carpet recycling center (open 8 a.m.–5 p.m. every day except Monday). To find the carpet recycling center closest to you, enter your ZIP code below.

Zip code: 95201

1. The carpet recycling center is closed on _____.
2. The carpet recycling center opens at _____.
3. The carpet recycling center closes at _____.

a. 8 a.m.
b. Mondays
c. 5 p.m.

D GO ONLINE. Find the recycling center closest to where you live. Write the information below.

Name: _____

Address: _____

Opening hours: _____

Items they recycle: _____

E BRAINSTORM. Many materials can be recycled. Read the list. How might you recycle these items?

Item	How to Recycle
bicycle	
clothing	
furniture	
mattress	

Lesson 4: Reading

A **DEVELOP YOUR ACADEMIC SKILLS. Read the Academic Skill. Answer the questions.**

1. Preview the title and image in Exercise B. What do you think the main idea of the text will be?
   a. why the Netherlands faces increased flooding
   b. new farming methods in the Netherlands
   c. how the Netherlands is responding to climate change

2. Skim the article. Find an emphasis signal word or phrase. Write it below.

_____

B ▶ **READ. Listen and read.**

How Will the Netherlands Cope with Climate Change?

1   The Netherlands faces a unique challenge when it comes to climate change. More than a third of the country sits below sea level. Due to its distinct geography, the country has dealt with flooding for hundreds of years. As a result, it has built a sophisticated system of walls along the North Sea. These walls help prevent flooding. However, as glaciers melt and sea levels rise, the walls will not be high enough to keep

5   out the water.

The world is paying attention to how the Netherlands prepares for climate change. Due to its geography, the Netherlands must act more quickly than other countries. The Dutch government's primary goal is to make the country more resilient to climate change. Let's take a look at three fascinating ways the Netherlands is working toward this goal.

10   The first strategy is that many cities are simply accepting flooding as the new normal. They are redesigning their cities accordingly. Cities such as Rotterdam, The Hague, and Amsterdam are building underwater reservoirs and lakes. During severe storms, water is diverted into them. The government is also building concrete tables and chairs throughout the cities. The furniture is attached to the ground. That way, it won't

15   get swept away during floods or damaged by water.

The second strategy is to find new ways to grow food and manage distribution. During heavy flooding, it can be difficult for trucks to make food deliveries. Therefore, cities are finding unique ways to grow

20   food locally. Many buildings now feature rooftop

gardens, which grow food that can be delivered nearby. The gardens also serve an added benefit of catching rainwater. Another noteworthy innovation is Rotterdam's floating farm. The farm is filled with cows, chickens, and rows of vegetables. It floats around Rotterdam's rivers and provides fresh food to restaurants in the city. Farmers in the country are also being innovative. One farmer discovered a kind of

25 potato that grows well in saltwater. Other farmers are starting to plant this potato across the country. That way, even if their fields flood with seawater, the potatoes won't be damaged.

The third strategy is to move people out of low-lying areas. Those areas are then deliberately flooded to keep water away from higher areas. Many people are upset when they have to move, but they accept it is for the greater good of the country.

30 It will be critical for the Netherlands to continue to find ways to cope with climate change. However, these examples show that the country is off to a promising start.

C **LOCATE DETAILS. Read the article again. Then read the statements and decide if they are true or false. Write the line numbers of your evidence.**

	T/F	Lines
1. More than 50% of the Netherlands is below sea level.	_____	_____
2. The Netherlands hasn't had to deal with flooding until recently.	_____	_____
3. Cities in the Netherlands are building reservoirs that collect flood water.	_____	_____
4. Rotterdam's floating farm delivers food to nearby restaurants.	_____	_____

D **CITE EVIDENCE. Read the article again. Complete the sentences.**

1. The sea walls in the Netherlands _____.
   a. may not be tall enough to cope with rising sea levels
   b. are definitely tall enough to cope with rising sea levels
   c. are built along the Atlantic Ocean

2. The world is paying attention to how the Netherlands copes with climate change because _____.
   a. it has invested a lot of money in alternative energy
   b. it will not be affected by climate change for a few more decades
   c. it is already experiencing more flooding than other countries

3. One of the food-related challenges that flooding causes for cities in the Netherlands is that _____.
   a. rooftop farms get too much water
   b. food delivery trucks can't drive in flooded streets
   c. floating farms can't grow food

Lessons 5 & 6: Grammar

A **COMPLETE. Complete the sentences.**

1. All this plastic wouldn't have ended up in the ocean if people _____ more.
   a. have recycled
   b. had recycled
   c. are recycling

2. If the world hadn't started to warm, the ice caps _____ to melt already.
   a. wouldn't have begun
   b. don't begin
   c. won't begin

3. If the factory _____ of its chemicals correctly, the river wouldn't have gotten so polluted.
   a. has disposed
   b. have disposed
   c. had disposed

4. When you fly on an airplane, you can donate an additional fee to offset your carbon use. If I had known about this when I flew to Europe, I _____.
   a. would contribute
   b. am contributing
   c. would have contributed

5. I _____ so much excess carbon dioxide last year if I hadn't traveled so much.
   a. wouldn't generate
   b. wouldn't be generating
   c. wouldn't have generated

6. If I had bought a hybrid vehicle last year, I _____ a lot less gas now.
   a. would have used
   b. would be using
   c. am using

B **COMPLETE. Complete the conversation using the correct forms of the verbs in parentheses.**

1. **Monica:** Did you hear that the city is going to ban plastic bags?

   Luis: Finally! If they _____ plastic bags earlier, they _____ a lot of
                                        (ban)   (prevent)
   pollution.

2. **Monica:** We just replaced all our light bulbs with energy-efficient ones.

   Luis: Good idea. I did that about a year ago, but I _____ a lot less on electricity if I
                                                          (spent)
   _____ them earlier.
        (replace)

3. **Monica:** Why are these vegetables in plastic packaging?

   Luis: I bought them at the convenience store.

   Monica: You know, if you _____ them at the farmers market, you _____
                               (buy)   (have)
   to throw away all this plastic.

   Luis: I know, but I didn't have time. If I _____ all the way to the farmers market, I
                                                (drive)
   _____ home in time to make dinner!
        (not be)

4. **Monica:** My kitchen faucet is leaking. I guess I should call a plumber.

   Luis: You should! Last year, my shower was dripping, and I let it go a long time before I

   called the plumber. I had no idea how much water we were wasting until I got my bill! I

   _____ a lot of water and money if I _____ the plumber earlier.
        (save)   (call)

5. **Monica:** It's a beautiful day. Why did you drive to the park?

   Luis: I wasn't thinking. If I _____ my bike, I _____ less gas!
                                    (ride)   (use)

C COMBINE. Read the sentences. Combine them in two different ways using the past unreal conditional.

1. Rita didn't get a raise. She didn't buy a hybrid.

If Rita _____

Rita would _____

2. Mrs. Shi didn't know about the new recycling center. She didn't recycle her batteries.

If Mrs. Shi had _____

Mrs. Shi would _____

3. Yolanda didn't tell Omar and Irma about the recycling center. They didn't take their bottles to the recycling center.

If Yolanda _____

Omar and Irma would _____

4. Mindy's clothes didn't fit her cousin. She didn't give her clothes to her cousin.

If Mindy's clothes _____

Mindy would _____

5. Joe didn't get a job closer to home. He has to drive a lot.

If Joe _____

Joe wouldn't _____

6. Our friends brought non-recyclable containers instead of glass ones. We can't recycle the containers.

If our friends _____

We would _____

D WRITE. Describe what would have or could have happened differently. Write new sentences using the past unreal conditional.

1. Passenger pigeons went extinct in 1914 because they were widely hunted by humans.

_____

2. People have diverted a large amount of water from Great Salt Lake, thereby causing it to almost disappear.

_____

3. The bald eagle nearly disappeared in the 1950s. The government banned hunting it, and now there are thousands of bald eagles in the United States.

_____

4. The area of Europe that is covered by forests has increased dramatically since the 1990s because European governments created strict laws about sustainable forestry.

_____

5. California's fires in 2019 were terrible because there had been so many years of drought.

_____

6. Plants help prevent mudslides because their roots hold soil in place. During the last rainstorm, there were terrible mudslides because people had cut down so many trees and plants.

_____

Lesson 7: Reading

A **DEVELOP YOUR ACADEMIC SKILLS. Read the Academic Reading Skill. Answer the questions.**

1. Preview the title and graphic in Exercise B. What is the purpose of the article? What information do you expect to read about?

   _____

2. Skim the article. Why does solar energy need to be stored in a battery?

   _____

B **READ. Listen and read.**

The Key to Making Solar Energy More Widely Available

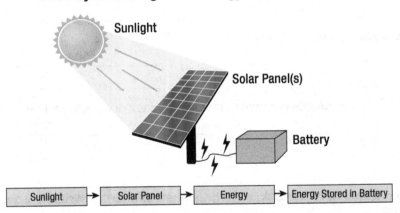

1   These days, solar energy is quickly becoming one of the cheapest forms of energy. It now costs $50 to

produce one megawatt of solar power. Coal, a more traditional form of energy, costs $100 per megawatt.

However, one key difference is that coal can be burned any time of day to make energy. Solar power, on

the other hand, can only be produced during the day when it's sunny. This is problematic because energy

5   demand peaks at night when it gets dark. The solution is to use batteries that can store solar energy until it

is needed.

Solar energy works by converting sunlight into energy through a solar panel. Then that energy gets

used or stored. Right now, there are batteries that can store solar energy and save it for later. However,

they are very expensive. Scientists around the world are working to develop cheaper solar energy

10 batteries. One inventive team hopes to create an inexpensive all-in-one solar panel and battery. If the team

succeeds, the battery could change the face of clean energy around the world.

In the United States, California is leading the charge when it comes to solar energy. That state's goal is to reduce greenhouse gas emissions significantly by 2030. One of the easiest ways to do this is to stop burning coal. The government is investing millions of dollars in solar panels. It is also investing millions of
15 dollars in solar energy batteries. California hopes to be a model for clean energy. The state wants to show that solar power can meet power demands any time of day.

Individuals hope to benefit from cheaper solar batteries, too. Right now, 3% of homes in the United States have solar panels. This number is growing rapidly for many reasons. Some people don't want to rely on the traditional energy grid. Other people make money by producing more energy than they need. They
20 then sell the excess to the power company. Still other people hope to increase the value of their homes by installing solar panels. The government gives people a tax benefit if they have solar panels. This is another incentive for many people. Experts say cheap solar energy batteries would dramatically change the energy market. If that were to happen, millions more Americans would suddenly be interested in installing solar panels on their homes.

25   Hopefully, affordable solar energy batteries will be a reality soon. They will help pave the way for the entire country to rely on clean, cheap, renewable energy.

C **LOCATE DETAILS. Read the article again. Then read the statements and decide if they are true or false. Write the line numbers of your evidence.**

	T/F	Lines
1. Solar energy costs $100 per megawatt.	_____	_____
2. Solar panels work by converting wind into energy.	_____	_____
3. California wants to stop burning as much coal as possible by 2030.	_____	_____
4. It's possible to make money by selling solar energy to power companies.	_____	_____

D **INTERPRET. Look at the graphic in Exercise B. What steps does it show? Match the steps with the appropriate step numbers.**

_____ **1.** Sunlight goes into the solar panel.   **a.** Step 1

_____ **2.** The energy is stored in a battery.   **b.** Step 2

_____ **3.** Sunlight is produced in the sky.   **c.** Step 3

_____ **4.** The solar panel turns the sunlight into energy.   **d.** Step 4

Lessons 8 & 9: Writing

Academic Writing Skill: Identify components of a valid argument
The purpose of an argument is to persuade someone to take specific action or to accept that a particular point of view is valid, or true. A valid argument is made up of a claim, main points, and evidence. A claim is the writer's main argument. Writers then use points to expand the claim and use evidence to support those points. Examples of evidence are facts, statistics, statements by experts, studies, and quotations.

A **STUDY THE MODEL.** Read two articles about environmentally friendly cars.

Article A

More people should think about buying hydrogen fuel cell cars. Unlike electric cars, hydrogen fuel cell cars use water and heat to make energy. This means that the car's only emission is steam. It also means the car doesn't rely on a battery. Another benefit of hydrogen fuel cell cars is that they charge in five minutes. This is about the same time it takes to put gas in a car. An electric car, on the other hand, can take anywhere from 30 minutes to a few hours to charge. Hydrogen fuel cell cars can also drive longer distances than electric cars. They can drive about 300 miles before they need to be charged again. Electric cars need to be charged every 100–200 miles.

Article B

There are many different kinds of cars on the road. Environmentally friendly cars are becoming more popular. More and more people are buying electric cars. These cars don't produce any carbon dioxide. They only use an electric battery for power. This means they need to be charged regularly. Another kind of environmentally friendly car is a hydrogen fuel cell car. These cars use water and heat to make energy. They also don't produce carbon dioxide. More people should start driving electric or hydrogen fuel cell cars. It would be better for the environment.

B **IDENTIFY.** Determine whether the components are a *claim*, a *point*, or *evidence*.

_____ **1.** Hydrogen fuel cell cars can also drive longer distances than electric cars.

_____ **2.** More people should think about buying hydrogen fuel cell cars.

_____ **3.** They can drive about 300 miles before they need to be charged again.

C **FIND DETAILS.** Reread the writing model. Which article presents the clearest argument with the most effective evidence? Identify the three parts of the argument. Can you also identify these parts in the less-effective article?

1. Claim: _____

_____

2. Key points: _____

_____

3. Valid evidence: _____

_____

_____

D ORGANIZE. Research different kinds of environmentally friendly cars. Choose one. List its advantages and disadvantages. Then state a clear, concise claim.

Car: _____

Advantages:

- _____
- _____
- _____

Disadvantages:

- _____
- _____
- _____

Claim: _____

_____

E WRITE. Write an argument about an environmentally friendly car. Follow the writing model. Remember to include a claim, clear points, and valid evidence.

F REVISE. Use the Writing Checklist to evaluate your writing and make revisions.

G COLLABORATE. Share your writing with a partner. Use any feedback to improve your writing.

H PUBLISH. Create a final document to share with others.

Writing Checklist	
	The text includes...
Structure:	✓ Argument
Organization:	✓ Introduction with claim restated in conclusion
	✓ Body with evidence to support claim
Word Choice:	✓ Academic words
	✓ Emphasis signal words
Writing Skill:	✓ Clearly stated claim
Grammar:	✓ Past unreal conditionals

Lesson 10: Workplace Soft Skills

A **DEFINE. Complete the sentence.**

Working effectively with a team means that you _____.
   a. can get other employees to agree with your opinions
   b. let co-workers take responsibility for solving problems and generating ideas
   c. collaborate with others to achieve workplace goals

B **EVALUATE. Read Situation 1 and the job applicant's response. Then answer the question.**

Situation 1

You work for a company that makes computer games for children. Your supervisor asks you and several co-workers to come up with some strategies for promoting a new game. Your main role on the team is to research and present examples of how other companies promote similar games.

Rate how desirable each of the responses would be.

Response	Undesirable	Slightly Undesirable	Slightly Desirable	Desirable
1. You conduct research, present your findings to the group, and let the rest of the team come up with strategies for the new promotion.	☐	☑	☐	☐
2. Instead of spending your time researching old ideas, you come up with a list of creative new ideas and ask the team to choose one of them.	☑	☐	☐	☐
3. As you present information about what other companies have done, you tell the group which approach would work best for your company.	☐	☐	☑	☐
4. You present information about what other companies have done, and you discuss whether a similar approach might work for your product.	☐	☐	☐	☑

The applicant's response is effective because it recognizes that _____.
   a. you need to be responsible for your own role while collaborating with others
   b. the team will work most efficiently if you make the decision about which approach to use
   c. you should move the project forward by providing as many creative ideas as possible
   d. you should only do the task that was assigned to you and allow others to do their tasks

C **ASSESS. How does the applicant work effectively with a team?**

_____

─ Occupation Profile: Game developer

Many people participate in the development of a video game. Game designers do things such as brainstorm ideas, create characters, write stories, conduct research, and design game layouts. They work with programmers who create and edit computer code. Game production also involves employees who focus on testing and correcting problems with the games. Most game developers have a bachelor's degree and experience in the field.

D ANALYZE. Read Situation 2 and respond to the situation. Then answer the question.

Situation 2

You work in the office of a plumbing company with four other people. Your boss is annoyed with the mess and disorganization in the office. People leave papers by the copy machine and empty coffee cups on tables, and they let the wastebaskets overflow before they empty them. Your boss says that everyone needs to deal with this problem.

Rate how desirable each of the responses would be.

Response	Undesirable	Slightly Undesirable	Slightly Desirable	Desirable
1. You make a list of clean-up tasks and assign each task to a co-worker. You post the list on the wall and ask your co-workers to follow it.	☐	☐	☐	☐
2. You ask your co-workers to meet and discuss the issue. At the meeting, you write down everyone's ideas and then present your notes to the boss.	☐	☐	☐	☐
3. You sit down with your co-workers. Together, you make a list of what needs to be done and who is responsible for each item.	☐	☐	☐	☐
4. You tell the boss that you always clean up after yourself and explain that the other employees need to take more responsibility.	☐	☐	☐	☐

My response is effective because it recognizes that _____.
   a. it's important to defend yourself when you are falsely accused of something
   b. the boss wants to have the final say about how to resolve the problem
   c. the best approach is to take charge of the situation and ask others to follow my suggestions
   d. the boss asked everyone to solve the problem, and the solution requires collaboration

E APPLY. Describe a situation in which you have worked or would work effectively with a team in the workplace.

_____

_____

_____

_____

Occupation Profile: Plumber

Plumbers install and repair pipes that supply water to homes and businesses. They also install and repair fixtures and appliances that carry water. Plumbers must usually be available for evening and weekend work and for emergencies, which can happen at any time of day. Most plumbers learn the job through an apprenticeship or on-the-job training. In most states, you need a license to work as a plumber. The number of available plumbing jobs is expected to grow in the next 10 years.

Unit 8 The Digital Age

Lessons 1 & 2: Grammar

A **COMPLETE. Complete the sentences. Choose all possible answers.**

1. The potential for misinformation to spread widely on social media _____ even worse in the future.
   a. is going to get
   b. will get
   c. be getting
   d. gets

2. As Earth gets warmer, people _____ technology to capture carbon emissions.
   a. develop
   b. are going to develop
   c. will develop
   d. developing

3. In the next 50 years, computers _____ many of the functions of lawyers and doctors.
   a. will take over
   b. are going to take over
   c. take over
   d. will be taking over

4. It's possible that TV in the future _____ many more interactive features.
   a. have
   b. will be having
   c. will have
   d. is going to have

5. Once the technology _____, doctors will be able to inject tiny robots into the bloodstream to search out and destroy cancer cells.
   a. will improve
   b. improves
   c. is improving
   d. is going to improve

6. Artificial intelligence _____ much of our art and music when the technology is advanced enough.
   a. is going to create
   b. is creating
   c. will create
   d. creates

7. In spite of all the movies about time travel, scientists _____ a time machine anytime soon.
   a. don't invent
   b. aren't going to invent
   c. won't be inventing
   d. won't invent

8. Someday, when we _____, we'll be able to wear a device in our ear that translates any language.
   a. will travel
   b. are going to travel
   c. travel
   d. are traveling

B **COMPLETE. Complete the conversation using the simple future or future continuous of the words in parentheses.**

Alan: Thank you for being on my podcast, Dr. Sanchez. I've heard your prediction that distance education _____ the traditional classroom. Could you explain your
(completely replace)
perspective for us, please?

Dr. Sanchez: It comes down to simple economics. Maintaining university campuses with old-school classrooms is expensive, and in the future, it _____ too expensive to be
(be)
worthwhile.

Alan: But what about the social aspects of university life?

Dr. Sanchez: As more universities move away from physical campuses, they _____ better
(get)
at facilitating interaction among students and creating online academic communities.

Alan: Do you think there _____ exceptions? Will any universities maintain
(be)
physical classrooms?

Dr. Sanchez: Yes. In some circumstances, students _____ access to specialized
(need)
equipment, such as medical equipment, and they _____ to get that at
(not be able)
home. But that _____ true for most fields of study. My guess is that by
(not be)
2040, students _____ almost all academic work over the internet.
(do)

C FIND. Read the paragraph. Find mistakes with verb tenses. The first one has been corrected. Find five more and correct them. Write in the corrections where relevant.

When people ~~will~~ hear stories about intelligent robots taking over jobs, they often wonder what humans are going to do for work in the future. Robots have already taken over many jobs that humans used to do, but what will happen when they ~~will~~ start doing more? According to many experts, intelligent machines will someday be diagnose most of our illnesses. They will teaching most of our children online and arguing for us in court. They are even be producing a lot of our art and music. In most cases, AI will do a part of every job, but it doesn't eliminate the job completely. For example, AI is getting better and better at diagnosis, but patients will probably want a human doctor at their bedside for the foreseeable future.

D WRITE. Read the "future headlines" from 2050. Do you think they will come true? Write predictions about what life will be like in 2050.

1. **No More Cords! Everything Is Wireless!**

2. *Use Contact Lenses to Check Your Email!*

3. **Use Technology to Communicate with Your Thoughts**

4. Scientists Use DNA to Bring Back Prehistoric Animals

5. ***Most Appliances Now Connected to the Internet***

6. **CGI Completely Replaces Live Actors**

7. Almost All Medical Diagnosis Now Done at Home

8. *Majority of Homes Have Robot Housekeeper*

9. **Humans Must Leave Earth**

10. *Human City on Mars!*

1. We will still use cords in 2050. Most electronics won't be wireless.
2. _____
3. _____
4. _____
5. _____
6. _____
7. _____
8. _____
9. _____
10. _____

A READ. Why did newspapers lose advertising revenue over the past decade?

Modern Media

Home | Today's Article | Archive | Blog | About Us

Fact-Checking Social Media

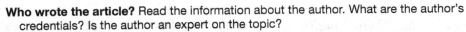

1 These days, nearly two-thirds of all Americans get their news from social media. Social media is unparalleled for its immediate and wide scope of news and information. The problem is that a lot of social media is filled with "fake news." Fake news is very appealing to readers. Studies have shown that fake news
5 reaches people six times more quickly than true news does. This is because people are significantly more likely to share false stories. On some social media platforms, fake news is 70% more likely to get shared than accurate news.

What should we do about all the unreliable news filing our newsfeeds? Experts say the most important tool we have is a strong fact-checking skill. When you open
10 an article from social media, evaluate it with the questions below. If you get used to evaluating every article you read, you will become a master fact-checker in no time.

Who wrote the article? Read the information about the author. What are the author's credentials? Is the author an expert on the topic?

What information does the author use to make his or her point? Look for evidence
15 the author uses. Is it up to date? Is the evidence from reliable sources, such as government or educational studies?

Can I find the information the author cites? Look for links to reports, statistics, and any other data the author uses to make claims. Check out some of the links yourself. Make sure they are from unbiased, objective sources.

20 **What information was left out of the article?** Did the author only present one point of view? If so, the article is likely biased and based on opinion more than fact.

What is the domain name of the website? Sites that end in .edu and .gov are most likely to contain reliable, unbiased information. Be wary of sites that end in .click, .work, or .io. They are more likely to have unreliable information.

25 **What is the date of the article?** Sometimes, people repost old articles on social media. This can accidentally make it look like something that happened years ago is current news.

Does the article make you angry or emotional? If so, it is probably biased and designed to stir up your emotions. Be wary of articles that target your emotions.

B LOCATE DETAILS. Read the article again. Then read the statements and decide if they are true or false. Write the line numbers of your evidence.

	T/F	Lines
1. More than 60% of Americans get their news from social media.	____	____
2. Real news is 70% more likely to be shared than fake news.	____	____
3. Reliable news should cite unbiased sources.	____	____
4. Websites that end in .io are more likely to have unreliable information.	____	____

C INTERPRET. Read the infographic. Then complete the sentences.

Majority say fake news has left Americans confused about basic facts

% of U.S. adults who say completely made-up news has caused _____ about the basic facts of current events

A great deal of confusion	Some confusion	Not much/ no confusion
64%	24%	11%

1. _____ of Americans think fake news has caused a great deal of confusion about basic facts.
   a. 11%   **b.** a majority   **c.** a quarter

2. Only _____ of people think fake news hasn't caused much confusion about basic facts.
   a. 11%   **b.** a majority   **c.** a quarter

3. About _____ of people think fake news has caused some confusion about basic facts.
   a. 11%   **b.** a majority   **c.** a quarter

D GO ONLINE. Find a news article. Evaluate it using fact-checking criteria.

Fact-Checking Questions	Answers
Who wrote the article?	
What information does the author use to make his or her point?	
Can I find the information the author cites?	
What information was left out of the article?	
What is the domain name of the website?	
What is the date of the article?	
Does the article make me angry or emotional?	

E REFLECT. What are the dangers of fake news on social media? Why is it important to fact-check articles you find on social media?

_____

_____

_____

_____

Lesson 4: Reading

A DEVELOP YOUR ACADEMIC SKILLS. Read the Academic Skill. Answer the questions.

1. Preview the title in Exercise B. What do you think the main idea of the text will be?
   a. tips you can take to avoid cybercrime
   b. how to choose secure passwords
   c. types of cybercrime and how it's changing

2. Skim the article. Find a conclusion signal word or phrase. Write it below.

_____

B  READ. Listen and read.

🔒 https://www.internetsecurity.org

How to Stay Safe Online

1   Even though many of us are online more than 25 hours a week, we don't always think about how to stay safe on the internet. As such, we may be unaware that there are many cybercriminals lurking online. They spread software called malware through insecure websites and email attachments. They can use the malware to get your personal and financial information. Sometimes, they even open credit cards under your name or take money out of your bank account.

5   For these reasons, it's important to take steps to stay safe online. Fortunately, these steps are easy and straightforward. Check out the following five ways to steer clear of cybercriminals:

Choose strong passwords. A surprising number of people choose weak passwords, such as 12345. Weak passwords are easy for cybercriminals to guess. For this reason, you should choose a password that is a random mix of numbers, symbols, and letters. A good password should be at least 15 characters long. Keep your passwords in a safe online
10   password manager so you don't forget them.
Keep your privacy settings on. Check all your social media accounts. Make sure your settings are on the highest privacy levels possible.
Only buy things from secure websites. You can spot a secure website in a few ways. Secure websites usually have a lock symbol in the web address. The web address should begin with https, not http. Looking out for that extra *s* will help you
15   ensure you are using a safe site.
Don't open emails or attachments from people you don't recognize. These could be carrying malware that cybercriminals can use to access your computer.
Subscribe to security software. Security software regularly screens your computer for malware and viruses. Although you usually have to pay for this software, it's ultimately worth the peace of mind you get from protecting your computer.

20   If you are the victim of a cybercrime, report it to the police immediately. Take screenshots and keep as much evidence of the crime as you can. Take your computer to a repair shop and make sure there are no traces of malware left on your computer.
Share this information with your family and friends. All in all, it doesn't take much time to follow these steps. And once you do, you can feel safe browsing online.

C LOCATE DETAILS. Read the article again. Then read the statements and decide if they are true or false. Write the line numbers of your evidence.

	T/F	Lines
1. Cybercriminals can use malware to access your computer.	____	____
2. Choose a safe password that is a mix of numbers, such as 12345.	____	____
3. A secure web address should begin with https.	____	____
4. If you are the victim of a cybercrime, you should get a new computer.	____	____

D IDENTIFY. Does the website in Exercise B look like a secure site? How can you tell?

1. _____

2. _____

E EVALUATE. Read the article again. Answer the questions.

1. What is the writer's claim?
   a. You can stay safe online if you follow a few straightforward steps.
   b. It's almost impossible to stay safe online.
   c. It's hard to know who's a cybercriminal online.

2. What change should you make to your social media accounts?
   a. Turn your privacy settings to the lowest levels possible.
   b. Change the password for your social media accounts every few weeks.
   c. Turn the maximum privacy settings on.

3. Why should you subscribe to security software?
   a. It can help you change your passwords.
   b. It can help the police track down cybercriminals.
   c. It can keep malware off your computer.

F BRAINSTORM. Reread the five tips the writer presented to stay safe online. Can you think of some other best practices for staying safe on the internet? Why is it important to follow these rules?

_____

_____

_____

_____

_____

_____

_____

Lessons 5 & 6: Grammar

A IDENTIFY. Circle the correct choices to complete the sentences.

1. Tim was lost. He couldn't find his way to the party because his navigation system **wasn't working / hadn't worked** and he **had left / was leaving** his phone at home. His car's navigation system **was starting / had started** having problems a few weeks before, but Tim **hadn't gotten / wasn't getting** it fixed yet.

2. The researchers **weren't being / weren't** surprised to learn that cell phones posed a risk for drivers of all ages. They **were finding / had found** the same results the year before.

3. Victor took a brief glance at his phone, but he **drove / was driving** too fast, so he **wasn't having / didn't have** time to stop once he **had looked / looked** up and saw that a car **had stopped / stopped** in front of him.

4. The driving instructors **told / were telling** students to keep their phones put away because they **didn't want / weren't wanting** anything to divert their attention from the road.

5. Jordan's justification for the accident was that James wasn't looking where he **had gone / was going**. From the damage to the cars, it's clear that James **had already pulled out / already pulled out** by the time Jordan got there.

6. Even though the office **was purchasing / had purchased** new software last year that was supposed to make Erika's job easier, she found that she **was / had been** still quite busy.

B COMPLETE. Complete the paragraphs using the simple past, past perfect, or past continuous of the verb in parentheses.

A man and woman _____ down the street in opposite directions, texting and not paying
              (walk)

attention to their surroundings. They _____ into each other, and the woman's phone fell, hit
           (bump)

the cement, and cracked. The man looked up for a moment to see what _____, but then he
           (happen)

kept walking. He _____ or stop texting.
      (not apologize)

Another man _____ while walking in the woods and a bear approached him from some
         (text)

distance away. He _____ the bear until it was very close, and when he finally looked up, he
        (not see)

panicked and _____ away. That story did not end in tragedy, but it could have. What if the
       (run)

man _____ the bear in time?
    (not notice)

These stories describe the events in two videos you can easily find by searching for "texting while

walking." Cell phones are not just a distraction while driving. There _____ more than 2,000
             (be)

texting-while-walking accidents last year, and many of them _____ in injuries.
            (result)

The lesson is clear: Don't walk and text!

C **WRITE.** Read the situations. Use your imagination to write sentences about what happened, what had happened, and what was happening.

1. Andy's phone wouldn't work.

    Past perfect: <u>Andy had forgotten to charge his phone.</u>

    Simple past: <u>Andy needed a new battery.</u>

    Past continuous: <u>Andy was doing something wrong.</u>

2. Alma wasn't happy with her new computer.

    Past perfect: _____

    Simple past: _____

    Past continuous: _____

3. The employees wanted a new software system.

    Past perfect: _____

    Simple past: _____

    Past continuous: _____

4. The driver ran a red light.

    Past perfect: _____

    Simple past: _____

    Past continuous: _____

5. Dom was surprised when he used the new social media app.

    Past perfect: _____

    Simple past: _____

    Past continuous: _____

D **WRITE.** Look at the picture. Use your imagination to write a short paragraph about what happened, what had happened, and what was happening.

_____

_____

_____

_____

_____

_____

_____

_____

_____

Lesson 7: Reading

A DEVELOP YOUR ACADEMIC SKILLS. Read the Academic Reading Skill. Answer the questions.

1. Preview the title and pie chart in Exercise B. What is the purpose of the article? What information do you expect to read about?

   _____

2. Skim the article. Why are smartphones distracting in the classroom?

   _____

B ▶ READ. Listen and read.

Children Should Not Have Phones in the Classroom
by Tony Saunders

1   Should students be able to have their phones in class? This is a pressing question for schools as phone ownership becomes increasingly common among students. More than half of all students in grades K–8 have phones. More than 80% of high school students have phones, and a whopping 99% of college students have phones.

5   I would argue that students should not be able to bring their phones into the classroom. I think it's fine if they bring their phones to school, but they should leave them in their lockers. Phones are very distracting. When students are allowed to bring phones into class, they

10   spend as much as 20% of class time texting, emailing, and checking their social media accounts. The average student checks his or her phone 11 times during the school day! Another issue is that some students use their phones to cheat. Nearly 35% of teenagers admit to

15   having used their phones to cheat on homework or tests.

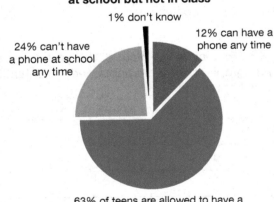

Majority of teens can have phones at school but not in class

1% don't know

12% can have a phone any time

24% can't have a phone at school any time

63% of teens are allowed to have a cell phone at school, but not in class

During class, students should pay attention to the teacher or work on projects with their classmates. They should not be on their phones. When students are distracted, they miss important content, fall behind on schoolwork, and are unprepared for homework and tests.

Almost 90% of schools in the United States have policies about phone use. Of these schools, 63%
20 allow students to have their phones at school but not in the classroom. When schools try to enforce such bans, however, they face resistance. Parents say they need to be able to reach their children if there is an emergency. Almost half of all parents say they use their children's phones to track them. They want their children to have their phones on them so they know they are safe.

These are valid points, but there are other ways to address parents' concerns. If there is an emergency,
25 parents can contact the school, and the school can send someone to the appropriate classroom immediately. If students are allowed to check their phones during breaks between classes or during lunch, parents can track their children then.

For schools to implement a total ban on phones in the classroom, they need to assign each student a locker with a lock. That way, students can keep their phones safe. Smartphones are expensive, and it is
30 stressful for both students and their parents if their phones are lost or stolen.

More schools should ban phones in the classroom. If they don't, distracted students and cheating will become more and more common.

C **FIND EVIDENCE. Read the article again. Find evidence that supports each point.**

Points	Evidence
Most students have phones these days.	• • •
Students should not be able to bring phones into the classroom.	• • •
Many schools have policies about phone use, but they face resistance from parents.	• • •

D **INTERPRET. Look at the pie chart in Exercise B. Match the percentages with the phrases to complete the sentences.**

1. _____ of students can have a phone at school any time.   **a.** 63%

2. _____ of students can have a phone at school, but not in class.   **b.** 24%

3. _____ of students can never have a phone at school.   **c.** 12%

Lessons 8 & 9: Writing

Academic Writing Skill: Use relevant and sufficient evidence to support an argument
A successful argument will be supported by relevant and sufficient evidence. As you write, consider the evidence you want to include to support your claim. Ask yourself, "Is the evidence relevant? Does it stay on topic? Is the evidence sufficient? Is there enough to support my claim?"

A **STUDY THE MODEL.** Read about the use of tablets in classrooms.

Books Versus Tablets in the Classroom

Students shouldn't use tablets in the classroom. First of all, tablets are significantly more expensive than print books. On average, they are 552% more expensive than new print books. Schools must not only buy the tablets but also pay for the electronic version of the textbooks.

A second reason is that print books don't need maintenance. They can't freeze or crash. They can't get hacked. Books don't require schools to have anyone on staff to fix them if they break.

A third reason tablets don't belong in classrooms is that tablets have too many distractions. Even if you restrict apps and websites, students still find ways to distract themselves. Almost 80% of students aged 8–18 multitask while using digital media. Students who are distracted in class don't pay attention to the teacher. They fall behind on classwork.

For these reasons, I think schools should use books instead of tablets in the classroom.

B **IDENTIFY.** Reread the writing model. What evidence does the writer use to support the claim? Write two sentences. Then answer the questions.

_____

_____

_____

_____

1. What is the writer's claim?

_____

_____

2. Is the evidence the writer uses relevant? Why or why not?

_____

_____

3. Is the evidence sufficient? Why or why not?

_____

_____

C ORGANIZE. Go online to find a source that argues for or against using mobile devices in the classroom. What claim does the writer make? What evidence is used to support that claim?

Source: _____

Claim: _____

_____

_____

Evidence: _____

_____

_____

D APPLY. What are your thoughts about using tablets or other mobile devices in the classroom? What argument would you make? Organize your thoughts below.

Claim: _____

_____

Evidence: _____

_____

My evidence supports my claim because _____

_____

My evidence is strong because _____

_____

E WRITE. Write an argument for or against using mobile devices in the classroom. Follow the writing model. Remember to incorporate relevant and sufficient evidence.

F REVISE. Use the Writing Checklist to evaluate your writing and make revisions.

G COLLABORATE. Share your writing with a partner. Use any feedback to improve your writing.

H PUBLISH. Create a final document to share with others.

Writing Checklist	
	The text includes...
Structure:	✓ Argument
Organization:	✓ Introduction with claim
	✓ Body with evidence
	✓ Conclusion
Word Choice:	✓ Academic words
	✓ Conclusion signal words
Writing Skill:	✓ Relevant and sufficient evidence
Grammar:	✓ Future predictions
	✓ Simple past, past continuous, past perfect

Lesson 10: Workplace Soft Skills

A **DEFINE. Complete the sentence.**

Exercising self-discipline with digital devices means that you _____.
   a. never use your phone during the workday
   b. do not allow your phone to interfere with your work
   c. only use your phone when you aren't busy at work

B **EVALUATE. Read Situation 1 and the job applicant's response. Then answer the question.**

Situation 1
You work at a warehouse where employees are expected to keep their phones in a locker during the day. Normally, you don't have a problem with this policy. However, your sister is in the hospital today expecting her first child.

   What are the most and least appropriate ways of dealing with this situation?

Response	Most Appropriate	Least Appropriate
1. Keep the phone with you and text a family member once an hour to see how your sister is doing.	☐	☐
2. Keep the phone with you and answer it every time it rings. If your supervisor notices, explain what is happening.	☐	☑
3. Explain the situation to your supervisor and ask for permission to keep the phone with you with the ringer on vibrate. Promise not to answer the phone while using equipment.	☑	☐
4. Explain the situation to your supervisor and ask for permission to take a break every hour to call a family member.	☐	☐

The applicant's response is effective because it recognizes that _____.
   a. it's OK to make an exception to company policy when something important is happening in your personal life
   b. if you ask for an exception to company policy, you should show that you understand the policy's purpose and will try to honor it
   c. people are used to cell phones and it won't bother your co-workers to hear your phone ring during the day
   d. employers understand they sometimes need to make exceptions to company policy

C **ASSESS. How does the applicant exercise self-discipline with digital devices?**

_____

_____

_____

Occupation Profile: Warehouse worker

Warehouse workers load and unload trucks, process orders, conduct inventories, and retrieve and organize boxes on shelves. They often drive forklifts and pallet jacks. They must be physically strong and must carefully follow all safety regulations. No formal education is required, but some skills, such as driving a forklift, require certification.

D **ANALYZE.** Read Situation 2 and respond to the situation. Then answer the question.

Situation 2

You work at an information desk inside a shopping mall. Your job is to answer people's questions and give directions. Your best friend sends you a text saying, "I have some incredible news!" At the same time, a customer comes to the information desk with a question.

What are the most and least appropriate ways of dealing with this situation?

Response	Most Appropriate	Least Appropriate
1. Greet the customer, but keep one eye on the phone so you can see what your friend says next.	☐	☐
2. Ask the customer to wait while you text your friend back to find out what happened.	☐	☐
3. Wait for a break in your conversation with the customer to quickly check your messages and text your friend.	☐	☐
4. Put your phone away and check your messages after you finish interacting with the customer.	☐	☐

My response is effective because it recognizes that _____.

    a. customers expect someone sitting at an information desk all day to use a phone
    b. it's fine to use my phone if I can still answer the customer's questions
    c. it's not appropriate to use my phone in front of a customer
    d. it's possible to deal with a customer and check my messages at the same time

E **APPLY.** Describe a situation in which you have exercised or would exercise self-discipline with digital devices in the workplace.

_____

_____

_____

_____

_____

_____

_____

_____

Occupation Profile: Information desk attendant

Information desks are usually found in places that attract lots of people, such as shopping malls, office buildings, schools and universities, airports, libraries, and tourist destinations. Attendants give directions and answer customers' questions. They must be friendly, have good communication skills, and have a professional appearance. They must be organized and able to handle multiple tasks at once. People working at information desks sometimes need technical skills, such as the ability to use scheduling software or direct phone calls.

Health in the Balance

Lessons 1 & 2: Grammar

A **FIND. Read the paragraph. Underline the passive verbs.**

A new yoga class is being offered at Silver Gym. This is a beginner's class for people of all shapes, sizes, and flexibility levels. Our instructors have received extensive training in both yoga and physical therapy. It can be scary to try something new, but in this class, you will be gently guided through the exercises by your instructors, and you will never be pushed to do something that is too difficult for you. All our classes are backed by a money-back guarantee. If you aren't satisfied after the first two classes, your money will be returned, no questions asked! So come on in and give yoga a try!

B **COMPLETE. Complete the chart using the passive form of the verbs in parentheses.**

Simple present	Regular exercise _____ for good health. (recommend)
Present continuous	The equipment is unavailable because it _____. (repair)
Simple past	This weight machine _____ to work for different body sizes. (modify)
Past continuous	We couldn't go into the gym because it _____. (remodel)
Present perfect	This gym is old, but it _____ very well. (maintain)
Simple future	They say the exercise bike _____ next month. (replace)
Modal: *should*	Nutritional information _____ for each item in the cafeteria. (posted)
Modal: *might*	Some of the unhealthy foods _____ from the menu soon. (remove)

C **COMPLETE. Complete the sentences using words in the box.**

added	are	can	is

1. Although it is most popular in the United States, Canada, Australia, and England, breakfast cereal _____ eaten all over the world.

2. Breakfast cereal _____ be made from a wide variety of grains, including wheat, oats, corn, and rice.

3. Cereals that _____ eaten hot, such as oatmeal, are often a healthier option than cold cereals.

4. Although nutrients are usually _____ to packaged breakfast cereal, it is still a heavily processed food not recommended by nutritionists.

D REWRITE. Rewrite the active sentences as passive sentences. Use the same tense.

1. They encourage everyone to eat unprocessed foods and get plenty of exercise and sleep.

   _____

2. They gave the employees a discount on health insurance for going to the gym.

   _____

3. Someone made us aware of a problem with the food.

   _____

4. They will reopen the gym next month.

   _____

5. They have offered yoga classes at this gym for several years.

   _____

6. People have made too many premature decisions in the past.

   _____

E COMPLETE. Complete the conversations using the passive voice of the verbs in parentheses.

1. **Toni:** Did you hear that hamburgers _____ in the cafeteria starting next week?

(not serve)

   Mei: No, I didn't, but it's good news. They're terrible for you.

   Toni: I don't care. It's my body. My health decisions shouldn't _____ for me

(make)

   by the company!

   Mei: They're not making health decisions for you. Hamburgers can still _____ at

(find)

   hundreds of restaurants all over the city. If you want to eat them, it's your choice. But that

   doesn't mean you can buy them here.

   Toni: I guess. I just wish employees _____ before these kinds of decisions

(consult)

   _____.

(make)

2. **Liz:** I heard that some new exercise equipment _____ in the park last week.

(install)

   Pat: Cool! Do you know what equipment?

   Liz: Well, some push-up bars _____ near the playground. An old running track

(put in)

   _____, and signs _____ around it with instructions for

(fix up)   (place)

   stretching exercises.

   Pat: Fantastic! We can do our cardio and strength training *and* our stretching in the park for free!

   Who needs the gym? Who paid for all this?

   Liz: It _____ for with donations and taxpayer funding. Apparently, it

(pay)

   _____ by the city council last year.

(approve)

Lesson 3: Workplace, Life, and Community Skills

A **READ.** How does preventive care help reduce healthcare expenses?

Westview Insurance

Home | Today's Article | Archive | Blog | About Us

We Support Your Preventive Care

1   Westview Insurance fully supports your preventive care. We believe the best way to keep you healthy is to prevent you from getting sick. We cover three main areas of preventive care:

Wellness Visits: This includes an annual physical exam and immunizations. Are you and your family up to date on the following immunizations? If not, schedule a vaccination appointment today.

5
- hepatitis A
- hepatitis B
- flu (autumn and winter)
- measles

- mumps
- tetanus
- chicken pox
- meningococcal (MCV)

Screenings: You should get your blood pressure, cholesterol, hearing, and vision checked regularly. If you are
10   overweight, you should get screened for diabetes.

Nutrition Counseling: Many diseases and cancers are caused by obesity. Maintaining a healthy weight is one of the easiest ways to stay fit. Book an appointment with a nutritionist today. Learn how you can improve your diet.

Preventive care is important for several reasons. First, you should see a doctor at least once a year even if you are
15   healthy. It's possible to develop health problems before you show any symptoms. Your doctor can give you tests to rule out any developing illnesses.
Second, seeing a doctor regularly helps reduce your healthcare expenses. Did you know healthcare expenses are the number one cause of bankruptcy in the United States? One reason is that many Americans use the emergency room (ER) as their main source of healthcare. In the United States, there are almost 140 million ER visits a year, which are
20   often very expensive. A single visit can cost thousands of dollars. You should rely on your primary doctor for medical care. You should go to the ER only if you have a true emergency.
Third, when you take care of your health, your quality of life improves. For example, if you smoke, talk to your doctor about how to quit. Smoking causes many health problems. These include strokes, heart disease, cancer, and chronic obstructive pulmonary disease (COPD). These illnesses reduce your quality of life.
25   The Westview Insurance team wants you to get preventive care. Book an appointment today. We look forward to helping you get and stay healthy!

B **LOCATE DETAILS.** Read the article again. Then read the statements and decide if they are true or false. Write the line numbers of your evidence.

	T/F	Lines
1. Preventive care includes an annual physical exam.	____	____
2. Obesity is linked to several diseases and types of cancer.	____	____
3. You should see a doctor at least once every five years.	____	____
4. There are almost 40 million ER visits in the United States each year.	____	____

C INTERPRET. Read the form. Then complete the sentences.

NEW PATIENT FORM: PREVENTIVE CARE QUESTIONNAIRE

Name: Pat Marco

Date: 2/19/21

1. What are your goals for nutritional counseling?
   I want to learn how to add more vegetables to my diet. I also want to lose 10 pounds.

2. What medications and vitamins do you take?
   I take an antihistamine and vitamin C every day.

3. How much do you sleep every night?
   6–7 hours

4. How much do you exercise?
   I try to walk at least three miles a day.

5. Do you eat breakfast every day? What do you usually eat?
   Yes. I eat a piece of toast, an egg, and yogurt every morning.

6. What are your favorite snacks?
   chips, hummus and crackers, and almonds

7. How many times a week do you cook your own meals?
   I don't like cooking. I only cook once or twice a week. I mostly eat frozen and prepared foods.

---

1. One of Pat's goals for nutritional counseling is _____.
   a. to add more fruit to her diet   **b.** to eat less junk food   **c.** to lose 10 pounds

2. Pat sleeps _____.
   a. more than 7 hours a night   **b.** 7 hours or less a night   **c.** 4–6 hours a night

3. Pat eats _____ for breakfast.
   a. toast, an egg, and an apple   **b.** cereal, a banana, and yogurt   **c.** toast, an egg, and yogurt

4. Pat eats mostly _____.
   a. frozen or premade foods   **b.** fresh meals she makes herself   **c.** junk food

D WRITE. Fill out the nutritional counseling form in Exercise C with your own information.

E REFLECT. What kinds of preventive care have you received in the past? How did it help you stay or get healthy?

_____

_____

_____

_____

_____

Lesson 4: Reading

A **DEVELOP YOUR ACADEMIC SKILLS. Read the Academic Skill. Answer the questions.**

1. Preview the title and images in Exercise B. What do you think the main idea of the text will be?
   a. how farmers' markets can solve the problem of food deserts
   b. why so many families live in food deserts
   c. how communities can tackle food deserts and food insecurity

2. Skim the article. Find a signal word or phrase that introduces facts and opinions. Write it below.

_____

B ▶ **READ. Listen and read.**

How Communities Should Respond to Food Deserts and Food Insecurity
by Asa Lee

1   More than 23 million Americans in cities live more than a mile from the nearest supermarket. These

communities are known as food deserts. Nutrition experts say people who live in urban food deserts don't

eat as many fruits, vegetables, and whole grains as they should. This is especially tragic when it comes

to children. More than 6.5 million children live in urban food deserts. Additionally, more than 17 million

5   children are food insecure. That means their parents and guardians can't afford groceries. These families

experience hunger multiple times throughout the year.

There are many ways for cities to address food deserts and food

insecurity. One is to support the Supplemental Nutrition Assistance

Program (also known as SNAP). In an average month, SNAP helps

10 42 million low-income Americans afford nutritious food. Almost

70% of SNAP participants have children. Even though SNAP covers

a small amount—approximately $1.40 per person per meal—it

still helps families eat healthier, and it lessens hunger. In fact, research shows that SNAP reduces food

insecurity by as much as 30%. SNAP is also linked to lower healthcare costs. The results are undeniable.

15 The average SNAP participant spends $1,400 less in medical care costs each year, compared to a low-

income non-participant.

There are many other ways to bring fresh fruits and vegetables into urban food deserts. Communities

can ask farmers' markets to open once a week in food deserts. They can promote and protect community gardens. They can organize backyard garden drives where people donate gardening tools and seeds. They

20 can teach people how to grow vegetables in their homes and yards. Cities can also ensure that there are

easy ways for everyone to get to the supermarket. This might mean creating new bus routes or providing

free shuttles.

Another innovative solution to food deserts is mobile grocery stores. This is a grocery store on wheels that can travel around a city.

25 Mobile grocery stores travel to and open in different neighborhoods on different days of the week. They sell food for less than nearby convenience stores. They also sell fresh fruits and vegetables. People can plan to buy groceries on the day the mobile grocery store is open in their neighborhood.

30 In my opinion, food deserts and food insecurity are unacceptable. I think we should be doing everything we can to give people access to affordable and nutritious food. The innovative solutions I describe are easy to implement. I believe more communities need to talk about adopting them.

C **LOCATE DETAILS.** Read the article again. Then read the statements and decide if they are true or false. Write the line numbers of your evidence.

	T/F	Lines
1. More than 23 million children live in urban food deserts.	____	____
2. Almost 70% of SNAP participants have children.	____	____
3. The average SNAP participant spends $400 less in yearly healthcare costs than a non-participant.	____	____
4. Mobile grocery stores sell less expensive food than nearby convenience stores.	____	____

D **EVALUATE.** Read the article again. Answer the questions.

1. What is the writer's claim?
   a. Communities should adopt solutions to tackle food deserts and food insecurity.
   b. Community gardens are the best way to fix food deserts.
   c. Communities should invest less money in SNAP programs.

2. What fact shows that SNAP is effective?
   a. SNAP covers $1.40 per person per meal.
   b. SNAP reduces food insecurity by as much as 30%.
   c. SNAP helps low-income families afford nutritious food.

3. What is the purpose of a backyard garden drive?
   a. It gives people the tools, seeds, and training to start their own vegetable gardens.
   b. It gives people the tools and seeds to plant flowers in their backyard.
   c. It encourages more people to buy houses with backyards.

Lessons 5 & 6: Grammar

A **FIND.** Read the paragraph. Underline the active verbs. Circle the passive verbs.

A lot of research has been done on mental health in recent years, and the evidence is growing that not getting enough sleep can have a negative effect on mental health. Researchers have found that sleep problems are common in patients with anxiety and depression. Sometimes, difficulty sleeping is a symptom of those conditions, but in some cases, anxiety and depression are caused by sleep problems. Sleep also affects learning. In one study, participants were taught a skill and then some of them were deprived of sleep. Participants who didn't sleep were unable to remember the skill the next day. The same skill was remembered easily by participants who got a good night's sleep.

B **USE CONTEXT CLUES.** Match the sentence parts. Then label the sentences active (A) or passive (P).

A/P		
_____	_____ 1. The psychologists are	**a.** treated for anxiety?
_____	_____ 2. Has Sal been	**b.** better this week.
_____	_____ 3. Do you think her mental health	**c.** been discovered yet.
_____	_____ 4. The causes of depression	**d.** been seen by several therapists.
_____	_____ 5. Have you	**e.** have been studied for years.
_____	_____ 6. Preeti's mood was	**f.** trying to find the underlying problem.
_____	_____ 7. Charles has	**g.** is getting better?
_____	_____ 8. The underlying causes haven't	**h.** considered the importance of your diet?

C **COMPLETE.** Complete the sentences. Use each verb twice, once in active voice and once in passive voice.

cause	experience	harm	make

Psychologists _____ a distinction between three different kinds of stress:

* Acute stress _____ your heart to race and your blood pressure to rise. You _____ acute stress in situations like almost getting in a car accident or sudden, intense pressure at work.

* In episodic acute stress, the symptoms of acute stress _____ regularly over a period of time. For example, you might feel episodic stress if you have long-term health problems or ongoing stressful situations at work. Many illnesses _____ worse by episodic stress.

* Chronic stress _____ by ongoing life problems, such as poverty. These kinds of problems can _____ a person's mental health. Sometimes, people who _____ by the long-term effects of poverty or other problems don't understand why they are experiencing symptoms of stress.

D REWRITE. Check (✓) the six sentences that can be rewritten in the passive voice. Then rewrite them in the passive voice.

_____ **a.** Mike's anxiety persisted for months after the accident.
_✓_ **b.** Two famous psychologists wrote this paper.
_____ **c.** Scientists conducted several studies on this topic last year.
_____ **d.** Relaxation techniques can relieve some symptoms of anxiety.
_____ **e.** She sat quietly and breathed slowly and deeply.
_____ **f.** Exercise often improves Sara's mood.
_____ **g.** Stressful events happen to everyone.
_____ **h.** What constitutes good mental health?
_____ **i.** How do they diagnose depression?
_____ **j.** Which exercises do they recommend for relaxation?

1. _This paper was written by two famous psychologists._

2. _____

3. _____

4. _____

5. _____

6. _____

E WRITE. Use the words to write a sentence in the active voice and a sentence in the passive voice.

1. Jim / treat / therapist / three years

_____

_____

2. Ann / help / counseling / a lot

_____

_____

3. his mood / lift / beautiful music / always

_____

_____

4. Tom's / job / cause / stress

_____

_____

5. experts / not recommend / a high-fat diet

_____

_____

6. Kelly's / disturb / sleep / light from her phone

_____

_____

Lesson 7: Reading

A **DEVELOP YOUR ACADEMIC SKILLS. Read the Academic Reading Skill. Answer the questions.**

1. Preview the title and graph in Exercise B. What is the purpose of the article? What information do you expect to read about?

   _____

2. Skim the article. What are two forms of arthritis?

   _____

B ▶ **READ. Listen and read.**

The Arthritis Generation

1   A chronic illness is defined as an illness that lasts for three months or more. One of the most common chronic illnesses is arthritis. Although there are more than 200 types of arthritis, most people have one of two kinds. The first is osteoarthritis. This means the tissue around bones breaks down. The second is rheumatoid arthritis. This means the body attacks its own joints. All types of arthritis cause painful, stiff joints. Arthritis can be frustrating and debilitating. It can make it hard for people to move their hands and fingers. As a result, doing everyday things, such as cleaning the house or cooking meals, becomes challenging.

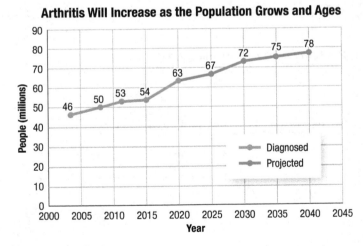

Arthritis Will Increase as the Population Grows and Ages

    The Centers for Disease Control and Prevention predicts that the number of people with arthritis will significantly increase in the next 20 years. This is because arthritis is most common among people who are 65 and older. As senior citizens age, they will become the arthritis generation. There are currently around 63 million adults with arthritis in the United States. Experts think this will jump to 78 million in the next two decades.

Treatment for arthritis is limited. Most doctors prescribe anti-inflammatory medicines. Research has proven that steroids are helpful for rheumatoid arthritis. People with arthritis can also try to minimize their

20 symptoms. For example, they can use special keyboards that support their wrists. If they have to lift heavy objects, they can wear a back brace. Despite these precautions, life with arthritis can still be difficult.

Dada Okafor is a 66-year-old eye surgeon. He developed osteoarthritis a few years ago, but it is getting worse. He is frustrated by how much it influences his life. He will have to retire soon because his hands are too stiff to perform surgery. It is also affecting his lifelong love of golf.

25 "The motion of swinging the golf club gives me pain up and down my back," he says. "After I play, I have pain in my wrists for hours, sometimes days. It's just not worth it anymore."

Marilyn Cressmore is a 70-year-old retiree. She has a beautiful garden filled with roses and vegetables. Unfortunately, she has developed rheumatoid arthritis. It makes gardening very difficult.

"I can't kneel in the dirt like I used to," she says. "I also have a hard time holding the gardening tools. It

30 even hurts to use scissors to trim my flowers!"

Sadly, Dada and Marilyn's stories are typical. As more and more people develop arthritis, they will be frustrated by how the illness affects their life. They will be disappointed they can no longer enjoy their favorite hobbies. Hopefully, people with arthritis will find ways to thrive in spite of their new condition.

C LOCATE DETAILS. Read the article again. Answer the questions.

1. Although there are 200 kinds of arthritis, _____.
   a. osteoarthritis and rheumatoid arthritis are the most common
   b. most people have one of five types
   c. osteoarthritis is by far the most common

2. Arthritis causes people to have _____ joints.
   a. loose and flexible
   b. painful and stiff
   c. healthy and strong

3. The number of people with arthritis is predicted to be around _____ within two decades.
   a. 65 million
   b. 68 million
   c. 78 million

D INTERPRET. Look at the graph in Exercise B. Match the numbers with the phrases to complete the sentences.

1. _____ million people will have arthritis in 2030.   a. 54

2. There will be an increase of _____ million people   b. 72
   with arthritis between 2020 and 2040.
                                                               c. 15
3. In 2015, _____ million people had arthritis.

Lessons 8 & 9: Writing

A STUDY THE MODEL. Read about heart disease.

Heart Disease: A Common but Preventable Condition

Heart disease is one of the most common chronic illnesses in the United States. It is a condition in which the arteries in the heart are narrowed or blocked. Heart disease is responsible for 1 in every 4 deaths in the country. Many simple tactics have been proven to reduce the risk of heart disease. For example, thousands of studies have demonstrated that one of the simplest ways to avoid heart disease is to exercise more. Quitting smoking also makes you less susceptible to the disease.

If you have heart disease, your doctor's goal will be to get you healthier. If you are overweight, your doctor will probably encourage you to lose weight and lower your cholesterol. There are two kinds of cholesterol: HDL and LDL. HDL is "good cholesterol." Your body needs it to function. LDL is "bad cholesterol." LDL blocks arteries that carry blood from your heart to other parts of your body. Medications can be used to manage LDL levels and help reduce the risk of a heart attack.

Research has shown that heart disease is more easily treated when it is detected early. If you ever have chest pain, shortness of breath, or dizziness, you should see a doctor immediately. If you do have heart disease, you should change your lifestyle and start treatment as quickly as possible.

B DETERMINE. Complete the following sentence.

The writing model uses passive voice effectively because _____

_____

_____

_____

C IDENTIFY. Reread the writing model. Answer the questions.

1. What are the problems caused by the illness? _____

_____

2. What are some solutions to these problems? _____

_____

3. What facts does the author use for support? _____

_____

D ORGANIZE. Go online and find a resource that describes a common chronic illness. What are the main symptoms (problems) of the illness? What treatments (solutions) have been proven to help the illness? Take notes about the information you find.

Illness: _____

Description: _____

_____

_____

Problem	Solution

E WRITE. Write about a common chronic illness. Follow the writing model. Remember to use the passive voice to create an academic tone.

F REVISE. Use the Writing Checklist to evaluate your writing and make revisions.

G COLLABORATE. Share your writing with a partner. Use any feedback to improve your writing.

H PUBLISH. Create a final document to share with others.

Writing Checklist	
	The text includes...
Structure:	✓ Problem-Solution essay
Organization:	✓ Defined problem
	✓ Stated solution
	✓ Facts for support
Word Choice:	✓ Academic words
	✓ Fact and opinion signal words
Writing Skill:	✓ Effective use of passive voice
Grammar:	✓ Effective use of passive vs. active voice

Lesson 10: Workplace Soft Skills

A **DEFINE. Complete the sentence.**

Displaying a positive attitude means that you _____.
  a. tell a lot of jokes and make people laugh
  b. are courteous, friendly, hardworking, and flexible
  c. come to work on time and do all your assigned work carefully

B **EVALUATE. Read Situation 1 and the job applicant's response. Then answer the question.**

Situation 1

You are part of a graphic design team at an advertising agency. Lately, you've had serious problems in your personal life, and you've been in a bad mood at work. You got into an argument with a customer, your team's work has been suffering, and your boss told all of you that you need to improve your performance.

What are you most likely to do in this situation? What are you least likely to do?

Response	Most Likely to Do	Least Likely to Do
1. Explain the personal problem to your boss, apologize for your behavior, and ask for her understanding.	☐	☐
2. Tell your teammates that they should be more sympathetic to your situation and should try to help you instead of making things worse.	☐	☑
3. Resolve to leave your personal problems at home and think of a way to motivate your teammates so everyone's work will improve.	☑	☐
4. Apologize to your teammates, and ask them if they'll put in a little extra work for the next week or two while you deal with your problems at home.	☐	☐

The applicant's response is effective because it recognizes that _____.
  a. you should apologize when you aren't displaying a positive attitude at work
  b. a team should pull together and cover for co-workers who are having problems
  c. it's important to explain to your co-workers why you've been in a bad mood
  d. you should try not to let your personal life affect your behavior at work

C **ASSESS. How does the applicant display a positive attitude?**

_____

_____

_____

_____

_____

Occupation Profile: Graphic designer

Graphic designers often work for publishing, advertising, or public relations companies as well as companies that specialize in design. They usually need a bachelor's degree in design and a portfolio of their work. Graphic design is a competitive field; designers who are also able to do website development are in demand and will find more job opportunities.

D **ANALYZE.** Read Situation 2 and respond to the situation. Then answer the question.

Situation 2

You work as a sales associate at a shoe store. Your manager asks you and a co-worker to conduct a store inventory. This isn't usually your job, and you dislike doing it. You'd rather help customers.

What are you most likely to do in this situation? What are you least likely to do?

Response	Most Likely to Do	Least Likely to Do
1. Explain to the manager that you'd prefer not to do the inventory, and ask if he could get someone else to do it.	☐	☐
2. Complain to the customers about your manager, and tell them that he treats you unfairly.	☐	☐
3. Make the work more entertaining by complaining to and making jokes with your co-worker.	☐	☐
4. Try to think of the inventory as change of pace, and encourage your co-worker to do it with you as accurately and efficiently as possible.	☐	☐

My response is effective because it recognizes that _____.
  a. it's important to accept whatever assignment I'm given with a positive attitude
  b. my manager can't expect me to have a positive attitude about tasks that aren't part of my job
  c. telling people about my situation will help me have a positive attitude
  d. one way to keep a positive attitude is to make jokes and bond with my co-workers

E **APPLY.** Describe a situation in which you have displayed or would display a positive attitude in the workplace.

_____

_____

_____

_____

_____

_____

_____

_____

_____

Occupation Profile: Shoe store sales associate

A shoe store sales associate greets customers and helps them find the right pair of shoes. Like most retail positions, many sales associates work part-time and do not receive health insurance or other benefits. In some stores, sales associates may earn part of their wages through commissions (a percentage of each sale).

Navigating Healthcare

Lessons 1 & 2: Grammar

A **FIND.** Read the conversation. Underline the embedded questions.

Dr. Cole: Good morning, Mr. Mun. How can I help you today?

Mr. Mun: Well, I've been feeling really tired lately, and I'm not sure what's causing it.

Dr. Cole: How long have you been feeling like this?

Mr. Mun: About three months.

Dr. Cole: OK. And can you tell me what your sleep schedule is like? Do you get enough sleep at night?

Mr. Mun: No, I don't. I go to bed at midnight and get up at 6 a.m.

Dr. Cole: That is definitely not enough sleep. Do you remember when you started sleeping for six hours a night?

Mr. Mun: Yeah. Three months ago. That's when I started working two jobs.

Dr. Cole: OK, Mr. Mun. I think I know why you're tired all the time!

Mr. Mun: Please tell me how I can get my energy back.

Dr. Cole: I'm sorry. I'm afraid you just have to get more sleep. Can you take a nap between jobs?

Mr. Mun: Maybe. I guess I'll try.

B **COMPLETE.** Unscramble the sentences. Write the words in the correct order. Each sentence has an embedded question.

1. he / do you know / has had / how long / blurred vision

   _____

2. was evaluated / I / I'm not sure / for diabetes / when

   _____

3. treats / a cancerous tumor / how / the oncologist / I wonder

   _____

4. how / can you tell me / this injury / you / got

   _____

5. why / was reluctant / with a specialist / he / I don't know / to meet

   _____

6. no idea / he has / when / started going up / his blood pressure

   _____

7. you / at the doctor's office / can you tell me / who / were speaking to

   _____

8. can treat / the ophthalmologist / she / how / isn't sure / my blurred vision

   _____

9. give me / they'll / do you know / for high blood pressure / what

   _____

10. doesn't know / is causing / what / the optometrist / her distorted vision

   _____

C REWRITE. Read the direct questions. Rewrite them as sentences with embedded questions.

1. Who is Don's cardiologist?

   _____

2. What time is my appointment with the dermatologist?

   _____

3. How long has he been seeing the oncologist?

   _____

4. When will she have surgery?

   _____

5. What can cause blurred vision?

   _____

6. How often does he confer with a specialist?

   _____

7. When does the neurologist get into the office?

   _____

8. How did he get that knee injury?

   _____

D USE CONTEXT CLUES. Complete the conversation between two co-workers. Use embedded questions.

Min-ji: Hi, Joe. Do you know _____?

Joe: Kate? Oh, she's at home. She's sick. She's going to be out for a couple weeks.

Min-ji: Oh no! What's wrong with her?

Joe: I'm not sure _____. She's having some kind of surgery.

Min-ji: Hmm. Could you tell me _____? I want to call her.

Joe: Sure. Her phone number is 555-2931.

Min-ji: Actually, I have a better idea. How late is FlowerMart open?

Joe: I know it opens early in the morning, but I don't know _____. Why?

Min-ji: I thought we could get Kate some flowers.

Joe: That's a good idea. She loves those colorful ones. Do you
remember _____?

Min-ji: You mean tulips?

Joe: Yes! That's what they're called.

Min-ji: It would be great to get her a big bouquet of tulips! I wonder
_____.

Joe: I have no idea. It might be expensive, but I'm sure Donna and Tom
would want to chip in a few dollars to help us pay for them.

Lesson 3: Workplace, Life, and Community Skills

A **READ.** What are the main differences between brand-name and generic drugs?

A Guide to Generic Drugs

1   Our customers ask us a lot of questions about generic drugs. In response, we put together a list of Frequently Asked Questions (FAQs) that will give you an overview of generic drugs so you can make the right choice when filling your prescriptions.

What are generic drugs?

5   There are two kinds of drugs: brand name and generic. Brand-name drugs are made by the company that researched and developed them. Drug companies spend a lot of time and money developing new drugs. Therefore, they are often given a patent on the drug. A patent gives them the right to be the only company that makes the drug. A patent can last for as long as 20 years. When a brand-name drug's patent expires, other drug companies can make the same medicine. Drugs that copy a brand-name medicine are called generic drugs.

10 **How are brand-name and generic drugs similar?**
Brand-name and generic drugs have the same active ingredient. An active ingredient is the medicine that treats a symptom or illness. Brand-name and generic drugs also have the same dosage, effect, duration, and strength. They must be able to be taken the same way.
15 For example, let's say you take a brand-name drug that comes in the form of a pill you swallow. The generic will also be a pill you swallow.

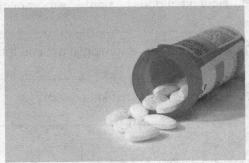

How are brand-name and generic drugs different?
The Food and Drug Administration (FDA) requires that each medicine on the market look different. Therefore, a generic drug will probably look different than the brand-name drug,
20 even though it is the same medicine. Another difference is that brand-name and generic drugs may have different inactive ingredients, which include coloring or preservatives. Inactive ingredients do not affect how the medicine works.

Are brand-name and generic drugs the same price?
No. In fact, generic drugs are usually 80–85% cheaper than the brand-name version of the drug. This is because companies that make copies of the brand-name drugs don't have to spend money researching and developing the
25 product. Four out of every five drugs sold is a generic. This saves patients, hospitals, and insurance companies billions of dollars each year. In some cases, your insurance company may require you to purchase a generic drug if it is available.

B **LOCATE DETAILS.** Read the article again. Then read the statements and decide if they are true or false. Write the line numbers of your evidence.

	T/F	Lines
1. A brand-name drug is a copy of a generic drug.	____	____
2. Brand-name and generic drugs have the same dosage and strength.	____	____
3. The FDA requires that all brand-name and generic drugs look the same.	____	____
4. Four out of every five drugs sold is a brand-name medicine.	____	____

C EVALUATE. Read the article again. Complete the sentences.

1. Generic drugs are usually 80–85% _____ than brand-name drugs.
   a. cheaper
   b. more expensive
   c. healthier

2. An active ingredient is _____.
   a. something that colors medicine
   b. a preservative that helps a medicine stay effective
   c. medicine that treats a symptom or illness

3. If a brand-name drug comes as a pill you swallow, the generic drug must be _____.
   a. a liquid you drink
   b. a pill you swallow
   c. an inhaler you inhale

D INTERPRET. Compare the information. Match the words with the phrases to complete the sentences.

Asthma Inhaler for Quick Relief	
BRAND NAME	**GENERIC**
Active ingredient: albuterol sulfate	**Active ingredient:** albuterol sulfate
Dosage: 1–2 puffs	**Dosage:** 1–2 puffs
Duration: 4–6 hours	**Duration:** 4–6 hours
Cost: $75	**Cost:** $30

1. The brand-name and generic drugs have a dosage of _____.   a. 4 to 6

2. The active ingredient in the medicine is _____.   b. $45

3. The generic is _____ less expensive than the brand-name drug.   c. albuterol sulfate

4. The brand-name and generic drugs last for _____ hours.   d. 1–2 puffs

E GO ONLINE. Look up a brand-name medication. Is there a generic version of it? What is the generic name?

Brand-name: _____

Generic: _____

Lesson 4: Reading

A **DEVELOP YOUR ACADEMIC SKILLS. Read the Academic Skill. Answer the questions.**

1. Preview the title and pie chart in Exercise B. What do you think the main idea of the text will be?
   a. what healthcare is like in Singapore
   b. how the United States can improve its healthcare system
   c. why so many people in the United States are uninsured

2. Skim the article. Find a word or phrase that signals a premise and one that signals a conclusion.
   Write it below.

_____

B ▶ **READ. Listen and read.**

What Can U.S. Healthcare Learn from Singapore?

1   In the United States, people get health insurance from a variety of sources. A majority of Americans—
almost 50%—get health insurance through their employers. About 6% of people pay for private health
insurance. Another 36% get their healthcare through the government. The programs administered by
the government are Medicaid, Medicare, and military insurance. Medicaid is managed by each state's
5   government. It provides healthcare to low-income families. Medicare and military insurance are run by the
federal government. Medicare provides healthcare for people 65 and older. Military insurance is for the
country's active-duty military and veterans.

The biggest problem with healthcare in the United States is that 9% of people lack any kind of insurance.
Consequently, they must pay the full cost of their medication and visits to the doctor. Given that, many
10   people without insurance hesitate to seek the care
they need. They worry it will be too expensive. A single
prescription medicine can cost hundreds of dollars.
A visit to the emergency room can cost thousands
of dollars. This is not a good long-term solution for
15   healthcare. The United States should adopt a few
practices from more efficient healthcare systems.

For example, Singapore has one of the best
healthcare systems in the world. Singaporeans can
choose to get insurance through the government or
20   from private companies. For this reason, all Singaporeans have health insurance. Singapore keeps costs low
in a few ways. The country caps the price of prescription drugs. It also operates a large network of public
hospitals. Basic care at a hospital is free. People who want better care and private rooms can pay for it.

Singapore values innovation and invests heavily in new technology. Their healthcare system is world-
class, yet the country spends four times less on healthcare than the United States does. Singapore spends
25   4.9% of its gross domestic product on healthcare. By contrast, the United States spends 17.2%.

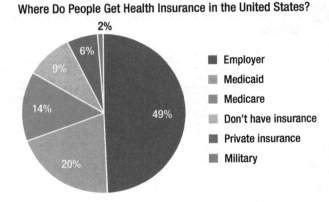

Where Do People Get Health Insurance in the United States?

- ■ Employer
- ■ Medicaid
- ■ Medicare
- ■ Don't have insurance
- ■ Private insurance
- ■ Military

49% 2% 6% 9% 14% 20%

The U.S. government should be more like Singapore. It should extend its government programs to more people. It could do this by lowering the age of eligibility for Medicare. States could also make more people eligible for Medicaid. If the United States took these steps, there would be fewer uninsured people. In addition, the United States could cap the cost of prescription drugs. This would save patients and the
30 government billions of dollars. The United States could also open public hospitals that could provide less expensive care than private hospitals.

The U.S. government should adopt these measures. Even though it would require years of changes, it would be worth it. It is unacceptable for 9% of Americans to be unable to get healthcare.

C **LOCATE DETAILS. Read the article again. Then read the statements and decide if they are true or false. Write the line numbers of your evidence.**

	T/F	Lines
1. Around 6% of Americans pay for private insurance.	_____	_____
2. Veterans can get their healthcare through the federal government.	_____	_____
3. Medicare is for people 65 and younger.	_____	_____
4. Singapore spends four times more on healthcare than the United States does.	_____	_____

D **EVALUATE. Read the premises and conclusion. Find evidence to support each premise. Write where you found the evidence.**

Premise 1: Millions of Americans lack health insurance. They can't afford basic medical care.

Premise 2: Singapore has one of the best healthcare systems in the world.

Conclusion: The U.S. government should mimic what Singapore does and extend government insurance to more people. That way, there would be fewer uninsured Americans.

	Evidence	Lines
Premise 1		
Premise 2		

E **INTERPRET. Look at the pie chart in Exercise B. Match the numbers with the phrases to complete the sentences.**

1. Military insurance covers _____% of the population.   **a.** 14

2. A total of _____% of the population gets insurance through Medicare.   **b.** 2

3. Medicaid covers _____% of the population.   **c.** 20

Lessons 5 & 6: Grammar

A **IDENTIFY. Read the direct questions. Check (✓) the embedded questions that are most similar in meaning.**

1. Does his residency begin next year?
   _____ Do you know when his residency begins?
   _____ Can you tell me if his residency begins next year?
   _____ I wonder whether he has begun his residency.

2. Are prescription drugs covered by this plan?
   _____ Do you know which prescription drugs are covered by this plan?
   _____ I wonder how many prescription drugs are covered by this plan.
   _____ I need to know if prescription drugs are covered by this plan.

3. Does the government regulate the price of medical procedures?
   _____ Do you think the government will regulate the price of medical procedures?
   _____ I'd like to know whether or not the government regulates the price of medical procedures.
   _____ I don't know why the government regulates the price of medical procedures.

4. Have they covered the administrative costs of the program?
   _____ Can you tell me if they've covered the administrative costs of the program or not?
   _____ I wonder how many of the administrative costs of the program they're going to cover.
   _____ Do you know which of the administrative costs of the program they've covered?

5. Did the pharmaceutical company pay for the research?
   _____ I don't know how much the pharmaceutical company paid for the research.
   _____ I'm not sure when the pharmaceutical company paid for the research.
   _____ I wonder whether the pharmaceutical company paid for the research.

B **COMPLETE. Complete the direct and embedded questions using words in the box.**

do	followed	if	is
not	or	regulate	whether

1. Do you know _____ the hospital administration is running smoothly?

2. I need to know _____ or not my insurance covers these payments.

3. Let me know if you find out how much the bill _____.

4. I'd like to know if the government is going to _____ drug prices.

5. I don't know whether or _____ we'll have to pay for the medication.

6. I'm not sure if they will charge us for the hospital stay _____ not.

7. _____ you know if there are rigid requirements for getting this coverage?

8. I'd like to know if they _____ all the necessary procedures to protect our privacy.

FIND. Each sentence has an error with the embedded question. Rewrite the sentences correctly.

1. I don't know if are there a lot of components to this problem.

_____

2. Can you tell me if or not the insurance is going to cover my surgery?

_____

3. Do you know does the optometrist accepts this insurance?

_____

4. I'm not sure are these tests are really necessary.

_____

5. I need to know do you get health coverage through your job not.

_____

6. Let me know whether have you seen the doctor in the last year.

_____

WRITE. Read the situations. Write two sentences with embedded questions you could say in the circumstances.

1. You have an unexpected charge on your insurance bill. You're hoping you can pay the amount next month, but you aren't sure. You call the insurance company and say:

_____

_____

2. You need to make an appointment to see the optometrist. You want to go on Saturday, but she might not see patients on the weekends. You call her office and say:

_____

_____

3. You believe the insurance company overcharged you. You hope the company is going to send your refund soon. You call the company and say:

_____

_____

4. You're pretty sure you already paid your insurance bill, but you decide to call the company to confirm. You say:

_____

_____

Lesson 7: Reading

A DEVELOP YOUR ACADEMIC SKILLS. Read the Academic Reading Skill. Answer the questions.

1. Preview the title and graph in Exercise B. What is the purpose of the article? What information do you expect to read about?

_____

2. Skim the article. How key parts are included in Medicare?

_____

B ▶ READ. Listen and read.

Medicare in the Future: Affordable?

1   Medicare was signed into law in 1965. This government program, which provides health insurance for people 65 and older, has tripled in size since then. As of 2020, more than 64 million people are covered by Medicare. That number is expected to explode as the population gets older. We can't afford this explosion in coverage given the way Medicare is currently structured. We need to change how Medicare works in
5   order to keep it sustainable in the future.

More than 10,000 baby boomers retire every day. Once they retire, they can no longer get insurance through their jobs. Therefore, Medicare or private insurance are
10   their only options. Experts think that, by 2050, more than 92 million people will be covered by Medicare. Medicare is already the second largest program in the federal budget. It makes up one-fifth of all health spending in
15   the country. This is a problem because soon there will not be enough money to cover the rising costs of Medicare. The data show that the current funds will be depleted in the 2030s.

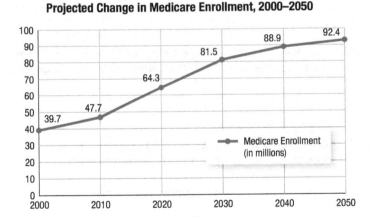

Projected Change in Medicare Enrollment, 2000–2050

We need to act now to address this shortfall. There are a few ways we can do this. First, we need to
20   look at how Medicare is structured. There are four key parts of Medicare. Part A pays for hospital care. Part B pays for visits to the doctor. Part C is a health insurance plan people can opt into to get better coverage. Part D covers prescription drugs.

The government should focus on finding ways to lower costs in each part of Medicare.

• To lower costs in Part A, more preventive care and drop-ins from home health aides could help
25   reduce unnecessary hospital visits.

- To lower costs in Part B, the government could invest in telemedicine. Doctors could help patients over the phone or video. The appointments would be shorter and less expensive.
- To lower costs in Part C, the government could offer more private insurance options. That way, people could cover more of their own costs if they wanted to upgrade their care. For example, they
30   could pay extra if they wanted a private room in a hospital.
- To lower costs in Part D, the government could negotiate the price of medicine directly with drug companies. It would then spend less money on drugs. The biggest increase in Medicare spending in the last 10 years has been on prescription drugs.

    The government also needs to find new sources of revenue to fund Medicare. It can do this by raising
35 taxes or diverting money from other programs. For Medicare to be sustainable, we need to make reforms now. We need to address the program's rising costs. We need to figure out how we are going to take care of people as they age.

C EVALUATE. Read the article again. Then fill out the author's arguments for lowering Medicare costs.

PART A
Premise 1: _Unnecessary hospital visits are expensive._
Premise 2: _Services such as preventive care and visits from home health aides would reduce unnecessary hospital visits._
Conclusion: _Adopting these services would lower the costs of Medicare Part A._

PART B
Premise 1: _____
Premise 2: _____
Conclusion: _____

PART C
Premise 1: _____
Premise 2: _____
Conclusion: _____

PART D
Premise 1: _____
Premise 2: _____
Conclusion: _____

D INTERPRET. Look at the graph in Exercise B. Answer the questions.

1. How many more people will be on Medicare in 2050 than there were in 2020? _____
2. How many people are projected to be on Medicare in 2030? _____
3. In what year was the number of people covered by Medicare the lowest? _____

Academic Writing Skill: Revise fragments and run-on sentences
A sentence fragment is a group of words that does not express a complete thought. Some fragments are missing a subject. Others leave out a verb. To fix a sentence fragment, add the missing subject or verb, or correct the verb form. You can also connect the fragment to a sentence before or after it (don't forget to add the correct punctuation).

By contrast, a run-on sentence has two or more independent clauses that are not connected correctly. To fix a run-on sentence, you can separate the clauses with a period. Alternatively, you can add a comma and a coordinating conjunction, such as *and, but,* or *so,* between the clauses.

A **STUDY THE MODEL.** Read the comments. Note that they include both sentence fragments and run-on sentences.

Medicare in the Future: Affordable?

Let us know what you think in the comments.

Ava394 8 hours ago

Millions of people are covered by Medicare, that number is only going to increase in the next decade. We need to fix Medicare now. We should increase taxes now to prepare for all the older people who are going to retire. If we don't. We will run out of money.

Ron19 7 hours ago

Medicare can't cover everyone. If older people had affordable private insurance options. More baby boomers could afford to buy their own insurance. Insurance companies need to offer more private insurance options.

Rosemary2586 1 hour ago

The cost of prescription drugs would be lower. If the government negotiated prices directly with drug companies. This is the biggest cause of rising Medicare costs. Drugs are too expensive for many people. They don't fill prescriptions they need, they take less medicine than they need to make it last longer. This is unacceptable. Everyone deserves to be able to get the medicine they need.

B **IDENTIFY.** Reread the comments. Choose two sentence fragments and two run-on sentences. Revise and correct them.

Sentence Fragments

1. _____

2. _____

Run-on Sentences

1. _____

2. _____

C RESEARCH. Go online and find a source that presents a possible solution for lowering Medicare costs. Take notes about the writer's main points. Remember to look for the writer's claim, premises, and evidence.

- _____
  _____
- _____
  _____
- _____
  _____
- _____
  _____
- _____
  _____

D WRITE. Write about a solution that will help lower Medicare costs. Remember to use logical reasoning and avoid sentence fragments and run-on sentences. Use the article in Lesson 7 as a model, if necessary.

E REVISE. Use the Writing Checklist to evaluate your writing and make revisions.

F COLLABORATE. Share your writing with a partner. Use any feedback to improve your writing.

G PUBLISH. Create a final document to share with others.

Writing Checklist	
	The text includes...
Structure:	✓ Argument
Organization:	✓ Introduction with claim
	✓ Body with evidence and conclusion
Word Choice:	✓ Academic words
	✓ Reasoning signal words
Writing Skill:	✓ Complete sentences without fragments or run-on sentences

Lesson 10: Workplace Soft Skills

A **DEFINE. Complete the sentence.**

Demonstrating professionalism means that you _____.
   a. behave in a calm, polite, and ethical manner while at work
   b. try to be the most successful employee
   c. always wear appropriate clothes to work

B **EVALUATE. Read Situation 1 and the job applicant's response. Then answer the question.**

Situation 1

You are an X-ray technician at a hospital. After you perform a routine X-ray on a patient, he becomes agitated and starts screaming that you hurt him, but you're sure that you didn't. He is very loud, and other people on the floor can hear him.

Rank the responses from most to least appropriate, with 1 being most appropriate. Assign a different number to each response.

Response	1	2	3	4
1. Tell the patient you'll get a nurse. Close the door when you leave so he won't disturb other patients.	☐	☑	☐	☐
2. Quietly ask the patient to describe his pain. Tell him that you will report the problem right away. Stay with him while you call a doctor or nurse.	☑	☐	☐	☐
3. Don't say anything and leave the room immediately. When you pass the nurses' station, ask a nurse to check on him.	☐	☐	☑	☐
4. Yell at the patient that you didn't do anything to hurt him and tell him to be quiet.	☐	☐	☐	☑

The applicant's response is effective because it recognizes that _____.
   a. it's OK to ignore a patient's complaints when they are obviously unreasonable
   b. it's important to reassure an agitated person that you will deal with any problems
   c. sometimes you can calm an irrational person by being forceful and aggressive
   d. the priority is to get away from upset people so they don't keep yelling

C **ASSESS. How does the applicant demonstrate professionalism?**

_____

_____

_____

_____

Occupation Profile: X-ray technician

X-ray technicians perform X-rays on patients. This job requires an associate's or bachelor's degree and, in most states, a license or certification. Some X-ray technicians continue their training and become certified in other medical imaging devices, such as CT, MRI, PET, and ultrasound. X-ray technicians work in hospitals, doctor's offices, clinics, and urgent care facilities. Employment in these jobs is expected to grow over the next 10 years.

D ANALYZE. Read Situation 2 and respond to the situation. Then answer the question.

Situation 2

You are the assistant manager of a pizza restaurant. It is normally your job to make the employees' work schedule each week. This week, however, your manager makes changes to several people's shifts. The employees are unhappy and direct their complaints at you.

Rank the responses from most to least appropriate, with 1 being most appropriate. Assign a different number to each response.

Response	1	2	3	4
1. Tell the employees to call the manager since she was the one who made changes. Explain that she interfered with your job and that you are angry about it.	☐	☐	☐	☐
2. Tell the employees that you will take their complaints under consideration. Call the manager in private and explain that the situation has caused problems. Ask for advice about how to deal with it.	☐	☐	☐	☐
3. Tell the employees that you will call the manager since she is the one who made the changes. Ask the manager if you can change the schedule back.	☐	☐	☐	☐
4. Call the manager and discuss the changes. Tell her that she shouldn't have changed the schedule without talking to you first.	☐	☐	☐	☐

My response is effective because it recognizes that _____.
- **a.** the manager needs to understand that she shouldn't interfere with my job duties
- **b.** I need to make sure the employees know the situation isn't my fault
- **c.** since the manager caused the problem, she is the one who should fix it
- **d.** it's important to remain calm and not cause more anger at the manager

E APPLY. Describe a situation in which you have demonstrated or would demonstrate professionalism in the workplace.

_____

_____

_____

_____

_____

_____

_____

_____

Occupation Profile: Restaurant manager

Restaurant managers (and assistant managers) usually have a high school diploma and several years of experience working in restaurants or the food industry. They may also have a degree in hospitality, restaurant management, or food service management. They often work evenings and weekends. Employment in this area is expected to grow in the next 10 years.

A **FIND. Read the paragraph. Underline the nouns used as adjectives. Circle the possessive nouns used as adjectives.**

My cousin Margarita moved to the United States seven years ago, and today I attended her naturalization ceremony. Margarita has wanted to become a citizen since she came here, but the application process takes a long time. First, she had to get a residency card and legally reside in the United States for five years. After the five-year period had passed, she was able to submit an application along with a fee. She received an interview appointment several months later. The interview was conducted at a USCIS office, and it included an English test and ten U.S. history and government questions. Margarita received the interviewer's recommendation for approval, and today I watched her take the Oath of Allegiance and pledge her loyalty to the U.S. Constitution. It was a great day. Unfortunately, Margarita's parents, my aunt and uncle, still live in El Salvador, and they weren't able to attend today's ceremony. Hopefully, they can visit soon to celebrate.

B **COMPLETE. Add apostrophes and hyphens to the sentences where they belong.**

1. Today was the ten year anniversary of his arrival in the United States.

2. The childrens parents made a commitment to become U.S. citizens.

3. Tania Browns decision to join the military was influenced by her patriotism.

4. The two boys names were mixed up on their application.

5. It is every citizens right and responsibility to register to vote.

6. My 71 year old father was granted citizenship last month.

C **COMPLETE. Complete the sentences.**

1. The interviewer asked me a series of _____ questions.
   a. history   **b.** histories   **c.** history's

2. I was surprised when it turned out to be a _____ interview.
   a. 15 minute   **b.** 15 minutes   **c.** 15-minute

3. They asked me to name one of my _____ senators.
   a. states   **b.** states'   **c.** state's

4. They also asked when we file _____ forms.
   a. income tax   **b.** income taxes   **c.** income tax's

5. They asked about the _____ reasons for coming to America.
   a. colonist   **b.** colonist's   **c.** colonists'

6. I had to know that all _____ can vote.
   a. 18-years-old citizens   **b.** 18-year-old citizens   **c.** 18-year-old-citizens

D COMPLETE. Complete the conversation using nouns as adjectives.

Amaya's	downtown	government	movie	parents'	train	two-hour

Lina: There's something wrong with this app. I'm trying to buy a _____ ticket, and it's not working.

Itsu: What movie are you going to see?

Lina: _____ Story. It's a story about a woman who moves to the United States from Spain.

Itsu: And her name is Amaya, right?

Lina: Good guess! She becomes a reporter and discovers some big _____ scandal.

Itsu: The U.S. government or the Spanish government?

Lina: Actually, I don't know! Do you want to come with me? It's playing at one of the _____ theaters tonight.

Itsu: Oh, I don't know if I want to go downtown. Last time I went to a movie there, we had a _____ wait in line.

Lina: Two hours! That must have been a really popular movie. There probably won't be any line at all for this one. And if there is, we can get dinner at the Vietnamese restaurant on Center Street.

Itsu: Oh, let's plan on doing that. Want me to pick you up about 6:00? I have my _____ car because they're both out of town on business. My mom is in New York, and my dad is in Chicago.

Lina: A ride would be great. The _____ station is going to be nuts at that time of day, and the trains will be really crowded.

E WRITE. Write sentences with the noun pairs. Make the first noun possessive, if necessary.

naturalization	process
interviewer	questions
immigration	officer
English	requirement
immigrants	applications

1. _____

2. _____

3. _____

4. _____

5. _____

Lesson 3: Workplace, Life, and Community Skills

A **READ.** How many regions are in the United States?

Regions of the United States

1   The United States is composed of many different regions. One common way people organize the 50 states is into six geographic regions. Read more about each region below.

New England: The states in New England are Connecticut, Maine, Massachusetts, New Hampshire, Rhode Island, and Vermont. Boston is the region's main city. New England is known for its beautiful 5 forests and beaches.

The Mid-Atlantic: The states in the mid-Atlantic region are Delaware, Maryland, New Jersey, New York, Pennsylvania, and the capital city of Washington, D.C. Other major cities are New York, Philadelphia, and Baltimore. The region has many mountain chains, such as the Poconos, Catskills, and Adirondacks.

The South: States in the South include Alabama, Arkansas, Florida, Georgia, Kentucky, Louisiana, 10 Mississippi, North Carolina, South Carolina, Tennessee, Virginia, and West Virginia. Some of the biggest cities in this region are Atlanta, Jacksonville, and Miami. The Appalachian Mountains run through much of the South.

The Midwest: The states in the Midwest are Illinois, Indiana, Iowa, Kansas, Michigan, Minnesota, Missouri, Nebraska, North Dakota, Ohio, South Dakota, and Wisconsin. Chicago is the region's largest 15 city. The Midwest is very flat. There are thousands of farms across this region.

The Southwest: The Southwest includes the following states: Arizona, New Mexico, Oklahoma, and Texas. Albuquerque, Las Vegas, and Phoenix are the biggest cities in the region. The Southwest is famous for its desert landscape. There are many beautiful natural parks, such as the Grand Canyon, the Petrified Forest, and Carlsbad Caverns.

20   **The West:** The Western states are Alaska, Colorado, California, Hawaii, Idaho, Montana, Nevada, Oregon, Utah, Washington, and Wyoming. The biggest cities in this region are Denver, Los Angeles, and San Diego. The geography of the west is very diverse. It extends from the blue waters of Hawaii to the tundra of Alaska.

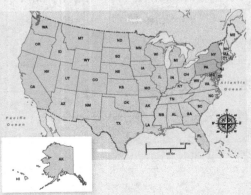

B LOCATE DETAILS. Read the article again. Then read the statements and decide if they are true or false. Write the line numbers of your evidence.

	T/F	Lines
1. The Poconos are a mountain chain in the mid-Atlantic.	_____	_____
2. Kansas is in the South.	_____	_____
3. The Midwest is famous for its beautiful desert landscape.	_____	_____
4. Denver is a city in the West.	_____	_____

C EVALUATE. Read the article again. Match the cities with the phrases to complete the sentences.

1. _____ is a city in the South.   **a.** Atlanta

2. _____ is a city in the Southwest.   **b.** Chicago

3. _____ is a city in New England.   **c.** Phoenix

4. _____ is a city in the Midwest.   **d.** Boston

D GO ONLINE. Look up information about the region where you live.

1. Where do you live? Circle the answer.

New England   Midwest

Mid-Atlantic   Southwest

South   West

2. Which state do you live in? _____

3. What's the biggest city in your region? _____

4. What are three tourist sites in your region?

a. _____

b. _____

c. _____

E REFLECT. Which region would you most like to visit? Why? What would you like to do there?

_____

_____

_____

_____

_____

_____

_____

Lesson 4: Reading

A **DEVELOP YOUR ACADEMIC SKILLS. Read the Academic Skill. Answer the questions.**

1. Preview the title in Exercise B. What do you think the main idea of the text will be?
   a. the first people who lived in what is now the United States
   b. the Europeans who colonized what is now the United States
   c. Ice Ages throughout history and how they affected humans

2. Skim the article. Find a signal word that identifies a step or event in a sequence. Write it below.

_____

B ▶ **READ. Listen and read.**

The First Inhabitants of North America

1   The last Ice Age ended around 12,000 years ago. Before then, much of Earth was covered in thick

sheets of ice. These sheets contained so much water that the oceans were much lower than they are

today. In fact, the oceans were so low that Siberia was connected to what is now North America. A large

land bridge twice the size of Texas linked the two continents. This was called the Bering Land Bridge.

5   Experts think that groups of humans started leaving Asia around 25,000 years ago. First, they settled on

the Bering Land Bridge for thousands of years. Then, as the Ice Age ended and the glaciers melted, they

moved east and south. Finally, they began to settle in what is now North America.

Anthropologists divide these earliest settlers of

North America into two groups: Arctic Indians and

10 American Indians. Arctic Indians lived in what we

now call Alaska, Canada, and Greenland. They were

nomadic, which means they moved frequently. They

hunted seals, caribou, and fish. During the winter,

groups of Arctic Indians coped with the freezing

15 temperatures in different ways. Some wore several

layers of animal skins to stay warm. Others stayed inside dome-shaped houses made of snow and

insulated with dirt. Some groups used sleds pulled by dogs to deliver food and supplies to one another.

American Indians settled throughout what is now the United States. One of the biggest cities was in

modern-day Illinois. It was called Cahokia, and it flourished between the years 600 and 1300 CE. At one

20 point, the city had as many as 20,000 residents. During this time, Cahokia became an important trading

post. Then the city was destroyed. Anthropologists think a flood wiped out the city.

The American Indians were also nomadic. Around 1000 CE, they began planting corn, beans, and squash. This allowed them to settle in villages. Once they established permanent homes, different groups were able to trade with one another. Eventually, they built elaborate trade routes throughout the country.

25   Many American Indian groups became known for specific rituals and arts. In the Midwest, the Pawnee, Omaha, and Sioux wore feathered headdresses. They held ceremonies and danced, told stories, and played drums. In modern-day New England, the Algonquin and Iroquois were known for their canoes made from birch trees. In the Southwest, the Zuni and Hopi were famous for their pottery, textiles, and sand paintings. They built adobe houses that were cool in the summer and warm in the winter.

30   Today, many American Indians still live in the United States. They continue to practice their cultural traditions and honor their unique heritage. For example, many American Indians in the Midwest continue to hold ceremonies, and many people in the Southwest still live in adobe houses. The government still has a lot of work to do to support American Indians in the United States. Their diverse history, culture, and ways of life are an integral part of U.S. history and deserve to be preserved and respected.

C **LOCATE DETAILS. Read the article again. Then read the statements and decide if they are true or false. Write the line numbers of your evidence.**

	T/F	Lines
1. A land bridge once connected Asia and North America.	_____	_____
2. Arctic Indians lived in the modern-day Southwest.	_____	_____
3. Cahokia was a large American Indian city.	_____	_____
4. Historically, the Zuni and Hopi were known for their pottery and textiles.	_____	_____

D **EVALUATE. Read the article again. Identify the steps in the process. Circle the correct answer.**

1. Humans left Siberia around 25,000 years ago and crossed the Bering Land Bridge **before / after** settling in North America.

2. Cahokia was an important trading post **before / after** it was destroyed by a flood.

3. American Indians developed elaborate trade routes **before / after** they began planting crops like corn, beans, and squash.

E **REFLECT. What did you learn about the first inhabitants of North America? Was anything surprising to you? What would you like to learn more about?**

_____

_____

_____

_____

Lessons 5 & 6: Grammar

A **COMPLETE.** Complete the sentences using words in the box.

convinced	damaged	disappointed	worried
convincing	damaging	disappointing	worrying

1. Getting our congressperson to sponsor our petition was a _____ experience. We were _____ because the bill never became law.

2. Our congressperson decided to sponsor our petition because we made a _____ argument. She wrote a bill, but it took several months and many revisions before the committee was _____ and finally approved it.

3. The senator voted for an extremely unpopular piece of legislation, and his reputation was _____. In the end, signing the bill was incredibly _____ to his reputation.

4. I'm _____ there won't be enough votes to pass the bill into law. Some committee members feel there are a _____ number of problems with the bill, and they want more revisions.

B **COMPLETE.** Complete the conversation using past or present participle forms of the verbs in parentheses.

Anam: Do you know who you're going to vote for? I'm really _____ to vote for Clara Perez.
(excite)

Lucas: Really? I don't know who that is. Honestly, I haven't thought about voting at all. I'm so _____ of politicians and their broken promises.
(tire)

Anam: Oh no! You've got to vote! And Perez is running for the House. She's a very _____
(excite)
candidate. She's got great ideas and a really _____ way of speaking.
(inspire)

Lucas: Well, I guess I'll check her out, but I've been pretty _____ with politics lately.
(disgust)

Anam: If you think politics is _____, you should vote so you can change it! You can't
(disgust)
really complain if you're not part of the decision-_____ process.
(make)

Lucas: I suppose.

Anam: Also, you're not just voting for the federal government, you know. There are some _____ local issues you might want to express your opinions on, too.
(interest)

Lucas: OK, OK, I'm _____. Thanks a lot.
(convince)

Anam: No problem at all. Be sure to check out Clara Perez! I don't think you'll be _____.
(disappoint)

C WRITE. Read the stories. Write sentences about each story using participial forms of the verbs in parentheses.

George Washington served as president during a very difficult time in U.S. history. After the Revolutionary War and the Philadelphia Convention, he didn't want to work anymore and was planning his retirement. But the people wanted him to be the first president, and he was persuaded to take the office. His plan was to serve for only four years, but at the end of his first term, the new government was having major problems and he was afraid to leave. There were very sharp party divisions in Congress, but people on both sides wanted Washington to stay in office. He is the only U.S. president who never belonged to a political party, and he was famously willing to listen to people with different points of view.

1. (*challenge*) _____

2. (*exhaust*) _____

3. (*concern*) _____

4. (*oppose*) _____

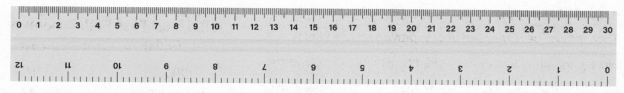

The United States is one of only three countries in the world that doesn't use the metric system of measurement. Instead, the United States uses U.S. customary units: ounces, inches, miles, and so on. This is sometimes difficult for visitors to this country and for manufacturers who want to import their goods to the United States without changing the measurement labels. In 1927, several million people sent thousands of petitions to Congress asking for a conversion to the metric system, but they had no luck because manufacturers opposed the change. Eventually, the Metric Conversion Act of 1975 was passed by both chambers of Congress and was signed into law, but progress was slow. Proponents of the metric system were happy that, in 1994, most U.S. products began using both customary and metric units on labels. In addition, some people took it as a good sign that NASA decided to start using metric units in 2007. Unfortunately, not much has happened since then because most Americans seem reluctant to change.

5. (*frustrate*) _____

6. (*disappoint*) _____

7. (*please*) _____

8. (*encourage*) _____

Lesson 7: Reading

A DEVELOP YOUR ACADEMIC SKILLS. Read the Academic Reading Skill. Answer the questions.

1. Preview the title and graphic in Exercise B. What is the purpose of the article? What information do you expect to read about?

   _____

2. Skim the article. Who creates new laws in the United States?

   _____

B ▶ READ. Listen and read.

How Does a Bill Become a Law?

1   One of the most important things the House of Representatives does is create new laws. All laws begin as bills. A bill is a formal explanation of a potential new law. Before a bill can become a law, it must be discussed and approved by the House of Representatives. Then it must be discussed and approved by the Senate.

5   Finally, the president of the United States must approve the bill. Once the president approves the bill, it becomes a law.

Bills begin as ideas. Representatives often get ideas for new bills from their constituents. A constituent is a person who lives in the area a politician represents. When

10   representatives have an idea for a bill, they do research on it. Next, they find someone to sponsor the bill. Often, the

A Bill Must Pass Both Congressional Bodies to Become a Law

HOUSE	SENATE
435 members	100 members

218 needed to pass   51 needed to pass

representative will find someone in the House who is an expert on the topic. For example, if the bill is about healthcare, the representative will ask a healthcare expert to sponsor it. Next, the representative tries to get support for the bill by talking to other representatives and encouraging them to back it. Once a bill has a

15   sponsor and support, it is ready to be introduced.

The process to introduce a bill is surprisingly old-fashioned. The bill's sponsor writes the bill. It gets assigned a number. Then the sponsor puts it in a special box in the House of Representatives. The box is called a hopper. After it has been put in the hopper, a clerk takes it out and reads it aloud to the representatives. The bill is then sent to a committee. There are many committees in the House of

20   Representatives. Each committee is composed of experts on different topics, such as agriculture, energy, or education. The committee reviews the bill. If they have questions or need more data, they send the bill

to a subcommittee. The subcommittee does research and collects opinions. Once the committee feels the

bill is ready, it introduces it to the House. All the representatives then discuss the bill and why they agree or

disagree with it. Usually, they make suggestions for ways to change the bill.

25   When the changes have been made, the representatives vote on the bill. If a majority of representatives

support the bill, it moves to the Senate. If a majority of senators support the bill, it then moves to the

president. The president can sign the bill and make it a law—or veto the bill. This means the bill is sent

back to the House of Representatives with a list of reasons why it wasn't signed. If two-thirds of all

Congresspeople (representatives and senators) support the bill, they can override the president's veto. This

30 means the bill becomes a law even without the president's support.

C LOCATE DETAILS. Read the article again. Circle all the words that indicate steps in a process.

D FIND EVIDENCE. Read the article again. Match the words with the phrases to complete the sentences.

1. A _____ is an explanation of a possible new law.   **a.** constituent

2. A _____ is a person who lives in an area a politician represents.   **b.** committee

3. A _____ is the box representatives put bills into.   **c.** bill

4. A _____ is group of people who are experts on a topic.   **d.** hopper

E INTERPRET. Look at the graphic in Exercise B. Answer the questions.

1. How many representatives are in the House of Representatives? _____

2. How many representatives are needed to pass a bill? _____

3. How many senators are in the U.S. Senate? _____

4. How many senators are needed to pass a bill? _____

F ORGANIZE. Make a graphic organizer that shows the process for how a bill becomes a law.
Show how one step leads to the next.

Lessons 8 & 9: Writing

A STUDY THE MODEL. Read the email. Notice how the writing is both clear and concise.

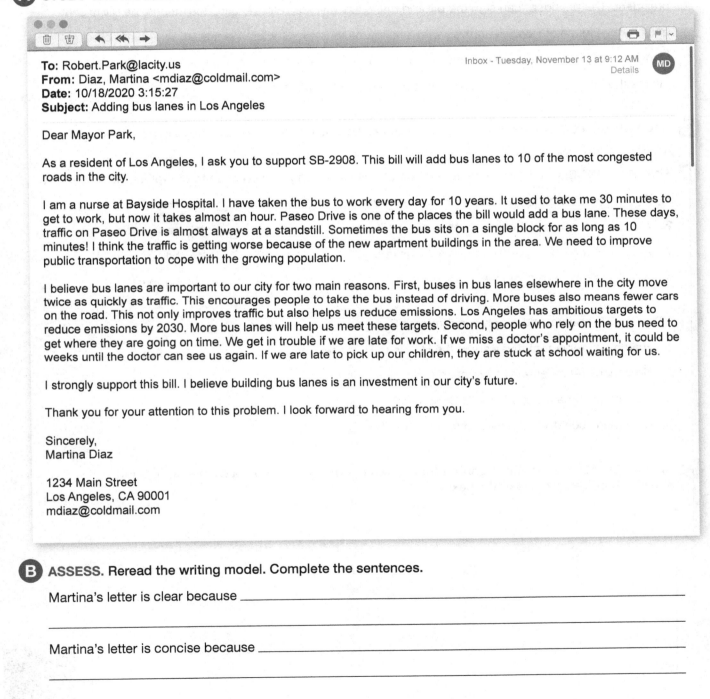

To: Robert.Park@lacity.us
From: Diaz, Martina <mdiaz@coldmail.com>
Date: 10/18/2020 3:15:27
Subject: Adding bus lanes in Los Angeles

Inbox - Tuesday, November 13 at 9:12 AM
Details

Dear Mayor Park,

As a resident of Los Angeles, I ask you to support SB-2908. This bill will add bus lanes to 10 of the most congested roads in the city.

I am a nurse at Bayside Hospital. I have taken the bus to work every day for 10 years. It used to take me 30 minutes to get to work, but now it takes almost an hour. Paseo Drive is one of the places the bill would add a bus lane. These days, traffic on Paseo Drive is almost always at a standstill. Sometimes the bus sits on a single block for as long as 10 minutes! I think the traffic is getting worse because of the new apartment buildings in the area. We need to improve public transportation to cope with the growing population.

I believe bus lanes are important to our city for two main reasons. First, buses in bus lanes elsewhere in the city move twice as quickly as traffic. This encourages people to take the bus instead of driving. More buses also means fewer cars on the road. This not only improves traffic but also helps us reduce emissions. Los Angeles has ambitious targets to reduce emissions by 2030. More bus lanes will help us meet these targets. Second, people who rely on the bus need to get where they are going on time. We get in trouble if we are late for work. If we miss a doctor's appointment, it could be weeks until the doctor can see us again. If we are late to pick up our children, they are stuck at school waiting for us.

I strongly support this bill. I believe building bus lanes is an investment in our city's future.

Thank you for your attention to this problem. I look forward to hearing from you.

Sincerely,
Martina Diaz

1234 Main Street
Los Angeles, CA 90001
mdiaz@coldmail.com

B ASSESS. Reread the writing model. Complete the sentences.

Martina's letter is clear because _____

_____

Martina's letter is concise because _____

_____

C IDENTIFY. Complete the sentence.

It is important for Martina's email to be clear and concise because _____

_____

_____

_____

_____

D ORGANIZE. Go online and find the bills currently being discussed in your city or state. Find a bill you support. Learn more about it.

Bill: _____

What it's about: _____

_____

Reasons I support it: _____

_____

_____

E WRITE. Write an email to a local elected official about a bill in your city or state. Use the writing model to structure your email. Remember to use clear and concise writing.

In the United States, sending a formal email to an elected official is an important way to participate in the democratic process. Keep your email formal. Use a respectful greeting and closing. Explain the problem and include background on the issue. Then suggest a specific solution.

F REVISE. Use the Writing Checklist to evaluate your writing and make revisions.

G COLLABORATE. Share your writing with a partner. Use any feedback to improve your writing.

H PUBLISH. Create a final document to share with others. Consider sending your letter to the appropriate elected official.

Writing Checklist	
	The text includes...
Structure:	✓ Persuasive email
Organization:	✓ Structure of a formal email
Word Choice:	✓ Academic words
Writing Skill:	✓ Clear, concise language
Grammar:	✓ Nouns used as adjectives
	✓ Participial adjectives

Lesson 10: Workplace Soft Skills

A **DEFINE. Complete the sentence.**

Respecting individual differences means that you _____.
- **a.** understand other people's behavior is not your business
- **b.** understand people have different needs, values, and cultures and should be treated courteously
- **c.** understand workplace rules may not apply to everyone

B **EVALUATE. Read Situation 1 and the job applicant's response. Then answer the question.**

Situation 1
You work in a pharmacy and are restocking one of the aisles. You leave several boxes at the side of the aisle while you help a customer. In the meantime, another customer in a wheelchair enters the aisle with the boxes. She says she can't reach an item she wants because of the boxes.

Rate how appropriate each of the responses would be.

Response	Very Inappropriate	Somewhat Inappropriate	Somewhat Appropriate	Very Appropriate
1. Apologize for leaving the boxes in the way and make a friendly joke about how she looks like she could just stand up and get the item herself.	☑	☐	☐	☐
2. Apologize, move the boxes, offer to get the item for her, and be sure to keep all aisles clear in the future.	☐	☐	☐	☑
3. Apologize, move the boxes, and offer to get the item for her. Don't take any additional action.	☐	☐	☑	☐
4. Retrieve the item for her but tell her that she won't be able to use the aisle because you're in the middle of restocking it.	☐	☑	☐	☐

The applicant's response is effective because it recognizes that _____.
- **a.** it's a good idea to share helpful advice to disabled people about their circumstances
- **b.** disabled customers shouldn't always expect to have the same level of access as others
- **c.** it's important to accommodate the needs of all people and treat them with respect
- **d.** it's important to make everyone feel comfortable by making friendly jokes

C **ASSESS. How does the applicant respect individual differences?**

_____

_____

Occupation Profile: Pharmacy assistant

Pharmacy assistants work at pharmacies in drugstores, grocery stores, and hospitals. They help pharmacists provide medicine to customers. They usually have specialized education and receive on-the-job training. In most states, pharmacy assistants (or technicians) are required to pass a test or complete a formal certificate program.

D ANALYZE. Read Situation 2 and respond to the situation. Then answer the question.

Situation 2

You are the assistant manager at a craft supply store, and you've noticed that a new employee seems to be impatient with older customers. Every time older customers require assistance or take a few minutes to make up their mind, the employee tends to avoid them or speak to them in an impatient manner.

Rate how appropriate each of the responses would be.

Response	Very Inappropriate	Somewhat Inappropriate	Somewhat Appropriate	Very Appropriate
1. Move the employee to a position where she won't interact with customers.	☐	☐	☐	☐
2. Ask management to fire the employee because she is rude to customers. Don't explain that she is only rude to older customers.	☐	☐	☐	☐
3. Report the employee's behavior to management and suggest that she receive training or be fired.	☐	☐	☐	☐
4. Tell the employee that her behavior is unacceptable and she needs to improve it or face punishment.	☐	☐	☐	☐

My response is effective because it recognizes that _____.

    a. sometimes people have reasons for their prejudices, and it's important to be understanding
    b. discrimination is a serious problem that should be dealt with immediately by management
    c. it's best to keep employees away from people they don't like
    d. there may still be a place for an employee who is not suited to customer service

E APPLY. Describe a situation in which you have respected or would respect individual differences in the workplace.

_____

_____

_____

_____

_____

_____

Occupation Profile: Assistant store manager

An assistant store manager assumes the manager's duties when the manager is not present. This means working with employees, answering customers' questions, and resolving customers' complaints. Assistant managers may also be involved with training employees, operating cash registers, and depositing money. They often work more than 40 hours a week and sometimes receive benefits, such as health insurance and bonuses.

Rights and Responsibilities

Lessons 1 & 2: Grammar

A COMPLETE. Complete the sentences.

1. Paul was supposed to register for the Selective Service last month, but he _____.
   a. might be forgetting
   b. could forget
   c. must have forgotten
   d. might forget

2. This used to be my polling place, but it's election day and there aren't any signs and no one is here. They _____ the location.
   a. must have changed
   b. must change
   c. might change
   d. could be changing

3. I got a notice in the mail to sign up for jury duty, but I'm not a citizen yet. It _____ a mistake.
   a. can be
   b. can't be
   c. must be
   d. couldn't have been

4. The economy is good right now, so the government _____ a lot of revenue in taxes.
   a. must be raising
   b. can be raising
   c. might have raised
   d. can't have raised

5. I'm not sure why Serge isn't voting today. I guess he _____ a citizen.
   a. might not have been
   b. may not be
   c. can't be
   d. couldn't be

6. Ann _____ on a jury two years ago. She wasn't a citizen yet.
   a. couldn't have served
   b. can't serve
   c. must have been serving
   d. might serve

7. The trial was in session for weeks. The people on the jury _____ very bored.
   a. must have been
   b. can be
   c. must be
   d. could have been

8. My neighbor said she doesn't have to file taxes, but that _____ right. Everyone has to file taxes.
   a. may be
   b. may be
   c. could be
   d. can't be

9. I sent a letter to my senator, but she never wrote me back. She _____ it.
   a. may not see
   b. might not have seen
   c. could see
   d. must not see

B FIND. Each sentence has an error with modals of deduction. Identify and correct the errors.

1. Tim said he would be at the meeting, but he must not come. I didn't see him there.

2. Jean crossed the street outside of a crosswalk and got a ticket. That must been illegal.

3. I didn't get my sample ballot in the mail. I must forgot to register to vote.

4. Look at all those people in the street! They must having some kind of demonstration.

5. Sara can't write this letter. It's full of mistakes, and she's always very careful.

6. Shawn said he saw Alice in court, but it couldn't be her. She was at work all day.

7. There's a moving truck outside. Someone must finally moving into the house next door.

8. I don't know what time he left last night. It may be around 10:00.

C **COMPLETE.** Complete the sentences. Use the verbs in parentheses with a modal of deduction to express a weak or strong theory. The verb may be negative.

1. I heard that Ken lied on his jury summons about being a citizen. He _____ that was punishable by law.
    (know)

2. Management has asked everyone to assemble in the lobby. They _____ something important, but no one knows what it is.
    (plan)

3. A lot of people don't bother to vote. They _____ that the right to vote is the foundation of our democracy.
    (understand)

4. Kylie said she didn't pay her taxes in April. She _____ them by now—I didn't ask.
    (pay)

5. You _____ that the rights you have were always guaranteed in this country, but they weren't. Our predecessors fought hard for them.
    (believe)

6. Sam says he always knew how the election would turn out, but I don't believe him. He _____ this crazy outcome!
    (predict)

7. Ann says she never voted because she didn't have time, but I don't believe that. I think she _____ it a priority.
    (make)

8. Kevin is having a serious conversation on the phone in his office. I think he _____ to his lawyer.
    (talk)

D **WRITE.** Read the paragraph. Use modals of deduction to answer the questions with your theories.

This November, Wanda is eligible to vote for the first time. She's excited to participate in the election. She made sure to register on time, she double-checked her registration online, and she researched all the candidates. She knows where her polling place is, and she plans to walk there early in the morning on election day. She has high hopes for the outcome of the election.

1. Why is Wanda eligible to vote for the first time?
    She must have just become a U.S. citizen.

2. How did Wanda research all the candidates?
    _____

3. Why is Wanda going to walk to her polling place?
    _____

4. Why is Wanda going to vote early in the morning?
    _____

5. Why does Wanda have high hopes for the outcome of the election?
    _____

Lesson 3: Workplace, Life, and Community Skills

A **READ.** What is the most common citation the police department gives?

Lafayette Valley Police Department

How to Avoid Traffic Citations

1　Being safe on the road should be a priority for everyone. If you drive recklessly, you might get a traffic citation. Here are the best ways to avoid getting a citation:

Don't speed. This is most common type of traffic citation we give. Pay attention to the speed limit around you. Drive at or below the speed limit. Be especially mindful near schools. The speed limit in school zones
5　drops to 15–25 miles per hour. This is to ensure that students are safe walking to and from school.

Don't use your cell phone while you're driving. More than 1.6 million accidents are caused in this country each year by people who use their phones while driving. One in four accidents is caused by someone who is texting while driving. Resist the urge to use your phone while you drive by keeping it in a bag or the glove compartment. You can also install a special app that automatically replies to people who text you while
10　you're at the wheel. It tells them you are driving and will reply when you get to your destination.

Don't drive without a valid driver's license. Check the expiration date on your license regularly. If your license is about to expire, get a new one as quickly as possible. You can be fined for driving without a valid driver's license.

Stop at stop signs. This may seem obvious, but we give a lot of citations to people who run stop signs. Every
15　time you get to a stop sign, be sure you come to a complete stop before you continue driving.

If you follow these rules, you should be able to avoid getting a citation in the future.

Thank you for your cooperation,
Lafayette Valley Police Department

B **LOCATE DETAILS.** Read the article again. Then read the statements and decide if they are true or false. Write the line numbers of your evidence.

	T/F	Lines
1. The speed limit near schools usually drops to 25–35 miles per hour.	____	____
2. One in four car accidents is caused by someone texting while driving.	____	____
3. You can drive with an expired driver's license as long as you plan to get a new one soon.	____	____
4. When you get to a stop sign, you should come to a complete stop before you continue driving.	____	____

C INTERPRET. Read the announcement. Match the words with the phrases to complete the sentences.

Lafayette Valley Police Department

Lafayette Valley Police Department
Community Meeting
Tuesday, November 17, 2021
6–8 p.m.

Sign up to volunteer for one of the following programs at this week's community meeting:

• **Join the neighborhood watch.** Help keep your neighborhood safe.
• **Help with neighborhood cleanup.** Pick up trash, plant trees, and paint over graffiti.
• **Help seniors.** Deliver meals and used books to your neighborhood seniors.
• **Ensure safety for families.** Learn how to
  – safely cross the street with your children.
  – childproof the windows in your house.
  – keep dangerous substances out of reach of children.

1. Keep your neighborhood safe with the neighborhood _____.
2. Plant trees with the neighborhood _____.
3. Deliver used books to neighborhood _____.
4. Learn how to childproof _____ and keep your home safe for families.

a. windows
b. seniors
c. watch
d. cleanup

D GO ONLINE. Some traffic laws are different in each state. Look up these traffic laws. Find out what they are in your state.

Traffic Law	Law in My State
maximum speed limit on the highway	
making a right turn at a red light	
child passenger safety	
age when someone can get a driver's license	

E REFLECT. Have you or has anyone you know ever gotten a traffic citation? What happened?

_____
_____
_____
_____
_____

Lesson 4: Reading

A DEVELOP YOUR ACADEMIC SKILLS. Read the Academic Skill. Answer the questions.

1. Preview the title and graph in Exercise B. What do you think the main idea of the text will be?
   a. why many Americans don't follow politics
   b. why many Americans don't vote
   c. how American voting has changed over the years

2. Skim the article. Find a signal word that indicates an inference. Write it below.

_____

B ▶ READ. Listen and read.

Why Do So Few Americans Vote?

1   Throughout the course of U.S. history, millions of Americans fought for and won the right to vote. Nevertheless, the United States has one of the lowest rates of voter turnout in the world. Only about half of eligible adults vote in any given election. Only 60% of people voted in the 2016 presidential election. Even less—53%—voted in the 2018 midterm election. If we compare these numbers to a country such

5   as Belgium, where more than 90% of the country voted in its last election, we have to ask ourselves an important question: Why don't we vote?

   One of the biggest problems is that one in four adults isn't registered to vote. Therefore, even if every eligible person voted, we'd never get above

10   75% participation. One way to solve this problem would be to improve our voting databases. We could automatically enroll people to vote when they turn 18. We could regularly update people's addresses and other relevant personal information.

15   This information could easily come from the United States Postal Service.

   Who else doesn't vote? Unfortunately, the data shows us that young people are the least likely to vote. Only one in four people aged 18–29 voted in the last election. And just 1% of young people are

20   frequent voters. What can we infer from this? Perhaps young people feel inadequately prepared to vote. As it turns out, research supports this inference. A survey conducted by Tufts University found that 20% of people under 30 don't vote because they believe they don't know enough about politics.

   We could increase youth voting in a few ways. The easiest way would be to improve civics education in high school. Right now, only nine states and Washington, D.C. require a full year of civics classes. We need

Frequent* Voters by Age

Age	Percentage
18–29	1%
30–39	5%
40–49	10%
50–69	23%
70+	41%

*frequent = have voted in six of the last eight elections

25 more civics education in schools. We also need these classes to include real-world scenarios, such as how to find a polling place and how to research information about candidates. Students would also learn what they should bring with them to the polls since these rules vary on a state-by-state basis.

What about low-income nonvoters? Despite the fact that they make up half of all workers, only 28% of people earning less than $30,000 a year vote. That means the other half of workers cast a disproportionate 72%
30 of votes in any given election. As a result, it's reasonable to infer that candidates will be more likely to make policies on behalf of those who vote. Therefore, low-income workers may not get the attention they deserve.

How can we increase the participation of low-income Americans? Millions of people earning $30,000 or less are hourly workers. They might not have the ability to take time off work. If they have children, getting to the polls before or after work might not be possible. One possible solution would be to make Election Day a national
35 holiday. That way, people would have the day off work, and they would be more likely to get to the polls.

It's important for all Americans to have a say in what kinds of policies become law in our country. We need to work together to improve voter turnout for our democracy's sake.

C **LOCATE DETAILS. Read the article again. Then read the statements and decide if they are true or false. Write the line numbers of your evidence.**

	T/F	Lines
1. Twenty-five percent of eligible adults aren't registered to vote.	_____	_____
2. Sixty-two percent of people aged 18–29 voted in the last election.	_____	_____
3. People are more likely to vote if they earn more than $30,000.	_____	_____
4. Election Day is already a national holiday.	_____	_____

D **EVALUATE. Read the article again. Answer the questions about the writer's inferences.**

1. The writer assumes that more _____ would improve youth voting.
   a. civics education
   b. outreach to young people
   c. U.S. history courses

2. The writer makes an educated guess that _____ would allow more people to vote.
   a. making voting mandatory
   b. making Election Day a national holiday
   c. opening more polling locations

3. The writer infers that people who earn more than $30,000 a year disproportionately affect policy because they _____.
   a. have more civics knowledge
   b. vote three times more than people who earn less than $30,000
   c. donate money to political campaigns

E **INTERPRET. Look at the graph in Exercise B. Match the numbers with the phrases to complete the sentences.**

1. _____% of people aged 30–39 are frequent voters.   a. 70 and over

2. 41% of people aged _____ are frequent voters.   b. 18–29

3. People aged _____ are the least likely to be frequent voters.   c. 5

Lessons 5 & 6: Grammar

A **IDENTIFY.** Read the paragraph. Underline the adjective clauses. Add commas if necessary.

The words of a Miranda warning which is given to anyone who is suspected of a crime and is going to be questioned vary from state to state. However, the warning always contains sentences that say something like this: *You have the right to have an attorney present during questioning. If you cannot afford an attorney, one will be appointed for you.* This part of the Miranda warning refers to a right that is guaranteed by the Sixth Amendment: the right to counsel. People who cannot afford to pay for a defense attorney are represented by public defenders who are lawyers that work for a publicly funded part of the government. In some places, the courts appoint private lawyers who have agreed to accept these cases.

B **USE CONTEXT CLUES.** Add the adjective clauses to the story. Add commas if necessary.

that Dave made who had never been stopped before who had gotten out of the police car	that was flashing its lights which was in his glove compartment with a lot of junk who were following him

The first mistake _____ was not stopping right away was when he saw the police car _____. He kept driving, hoping the officers _____ would change their minds and go look for someone else. When he realized that wasn't going to happen, Dave stopped the car and opened his door to get out. One of the officers _____ said, "Remain in your vehicle." Dave got back in the car. Then the officer asked, "Can I see your driver's license and registration, please?" Dave _____ didn't realize that he should respond immediately. Instead, he said, "Why did you stop me?" The officer said that Dave had been driving too fast and asked him for the documents again. Dave showed the officer his license, but it took him a while to find the registration _____. The officer suspected that Dave was hiding something and did a search of his record. Fortunately for Dave, he didn't have unpaid parking tickets or other problems, so the officer wrote him a ticket and let him go.

C MODIFY. Read the sentences. Some adjective clauses should be changed from restrictive to non-restrictive, or vice versa. Make corrections where necessary. Check (✓) the sentence if it is correct.

☐ **1.** The legal protections, which we receive from the Fifth Amendment, are very important.

☐ **2.** The man's confession that was difficult to believe was thrown out of court.

☐ **3.** The accountant invoked the Fifth Amendment, which said he did not have to speak against himself.

☐ **4.** We are seeking justice for Mr. Nelson that was accused of a crime he did not commit.

☐ **5.** The court reversed the Jones decision, which had been made by a lower court three years before.

☐ **6.** Mark who lives next door to me has many misconceptions about the law.

D REWRITE. Read the sentences. Make the second sentence an adjective clause. Use commas where necessary.

1. The first part of a Miranda warning refers to rights. The rights are guaranteed in the Fifth Amendment.

_____

2. The Fifth Amendment addresses criminal procedure. The Fifth Amendment is part of the Bill of Rights.

_____

3. There is one section. The section says everyone has the right to "due process of law."

_____

4. A person cannot be forced to testify in court. That person has been accused of committing a crime.

_____

5. That person may refuse to provide answers. The answers might suggest he or she did something illegal.

_____

6. A person is "pleading the Fifth." That person refuses to answer questions.

_____

E EXPAND. Look at the topics. Use your own ideas to write sentences with adjective clauses. Remember to use commas where necessary.

1. The Supreme Court: _____

_____

2. The U.S. Constitution: _____

_____

3. The Miranda warning: _____

_____

4. The Fifth Amendment: _____

_____

Lesson 7: Reading

A DEVELOP YOUR ACADEMIC SKILLS. Read the Academic Reading Skill. Answer the questions.

1. Preview the title and image in Exercise B. What is the purpose of the article? What information do you expect to read about?

   _____

2. Skim the article. What argument is the writer making?

   _____

B ▶ READ. Listen and read.

Let's Make Voting Mandatory
by Jim Addo, U.S. senator

1   Did you know that only about half of Americans vote in a given election? In Australia, upwards of 96% of people turn out to vote! What is the difference between our two countries? Well, in Australia, like many other countries, voting is mandatory. Australia automatically registers voters when they are old enough to vote. Then it makes voting as easy as possible. Australians can mail in their vote. Election days are on

5 Saturdays. If people don't vote, they need to pay a $20 fine. There are similar laws in place around the world—in Argentina, Brazil, and Singapore, to name a few.

    As a senator, this issue is deeply important to me. Are we a true democracy if only half of our population is represented at the polls? I believe Americans have a right to have their voices heard when we make policies. Our policies are only as fair as the number of people who support them. Therefore, I think

10 we should make voting mandatory. We should also make Election Day a national holiday. This would make it easier for people to get to the polls. If more people could get to the polls, then more people would vote.

    We can all agree mandatory voting would be a big shift.

15 It would take time to improve our databases. We'd have to figure out how to enforce this new law. We'd also have to prepare for a few bumps in the road. For example, what about people who are uneducated about the candidates? They might cast their votes randomly. We could address this issue by improving voter education. Volunteers could hand out flyers about the candidates before elections. Cities, states, and the

20 federal government could improve their websites. They could feature information about every candidate.

You might ask, "How does not voting harm anyone? Only things that harm people should be illegal."

I would argue that a lack of voter participation is harmful. Young, low-income Americans with low levels

of education make up the bulk of nonvoters. If they are not represented at the polls, do the elected

candidates truly represent all their constituents? If voter turnout is low, candidates with much less than a

25 majority of the vote can win. I see voting as a civic duty. I don't think it's different from jury duty or taxes,

both of which are mandatory and necessary to keep our democracy functioning.

Voting doesn't have to be hard or time-consuming, especially if Election Day were a national holiday.

Polling places are currently in convenient places that are easy to access. If Americans had the day off,

it would be much easier for them to get to the polls. Keep in mind that even if Americans voted in every

30 single national and local election, they'd still only be going to the polls once or twice a year. This is not a

huge burden on anyone's time.

We are a democracy. This means that "we the people" lead this country. We elect politicians to

represent our needs, not the other way around. Mandatory voting would put the voters back in charge.

C **LOCATE DETAILS. Read the article again. Match the words with the phrases to complete the sentences.**

1. _____ has a law requiring people to vote.

2. In Australia, if people don't vote, they must pay a _____.

3. One problem with mandatory voting is people's votes could be _____.

4. Civic duties such as jury duty and paying taxes are _____.

   a. fine

   b. mandatory

   c. Brazil

   d. random

D **EVALUATE. Read the article again. What inferences can you make about what the senator does not say? Answer the questions.**

1. The senator thinks _____ young, low-income Americans with low levels of education vote.
   a. enough
   b. not enough
   c. too many

2. We need to help educate voters so they know _____.
   a. which candidates best represent their interests
   b. which elections they can skip
   c. more about jury duty obligations

3. The senator thinks mandatory voting would _____.
   a. be too difficult to implement
   b. make our country less democratic
   c. make our country more democratic

E **GO ONLINE. Find information about the next election in your area.**

1. When is the next election in your city or state? _____

2. What position is the election for? _____

3. Where is your polling place for the election? _____

4. What do you need to bring with you to vote? _____

Lessons 8 & 9: Writing

The hasty generalization fallacy occurs when someone bases a general conclusion on insufficient evidence. Instead of a statement being true for a few examples or for a limited number of individuals, a hasty generalization is stated as if it were true for everything or everyone. For example:

The candidate I voted for lost. No one in my city agrees with me!

Adding a qualifier such as *some, few, often, likely,* or *probably* can change a hasty generalization to something more specific and believable. For example:

The candidate I voted for lost. Some people in my city likely have different priorities than I do.

A **APPLY.** Change the hasty generalizations to credible claims by using the qualifiers in parentheses.

1. No one cares about the environment. We will never elect politicians who make laws that protect the environment.

   (*some, probably*) _____

2. No one is in favor of the bill to build a new airport, so it's never going to be built.

   (*few, likely*) _____

B **STUDY THE MODEL.** Read the evaluation of an article. Why does the reader think the article was reliable?

Evaluation: Why We Need to Return to Paper Ballots

I read an article called "Why We Need to Return to Paper Ballots," by Alex Omar. His claim is that electronic voting machines are problematic for two big reasons. First, they can experience hardware or software problems. This can cause them to crash or tally voting results incorrectly. Second, voting machines can be hacked. At a recent hacking conference, it took hackers less than one day to break into five different types of voting machines.

The writer argues that we should return to paper ballots. Paper ballots can't be hacked. They're not vulnerable to failures. Also, with paper ballots, there is visible evidence of problems. This makes problems with the voting process easier to solve.

I think the author's claim is reliable. He used clear, logical arguments to make his point. He used evidence from state and national news agencies. I read the article on a local news website. The author is a state representative. I think he is qualified to write the article since he is an elected official and lawmaker.

The author also included a lot of strong evidence to make his points. He relied on facts instead of opinions. He didn't rely on any logical fallacies to make his case. I wish he had considered more counterarguments to his point, though. For example, electronic voting would allow people to vote from home. This would help more disabled and elderly people participate in the voting process. He didn't consider this point.

Overall, I thought the article was reliable and persuasive. He convinced me that we should return to paper ballots.

C **IDENTIFY.** Find a hasty generalization the author uses in the evaluation. Use qualifiers to change the hasty generalization to a credible claim.

_____

_____

D **DETERMINE.** Reread the writing model. Why does the reader think the article was reliable?

_____

_____

_____

_____

E **ORGANIZE.** Go online and find an article about how to improve the voting process in the United States. Summarize and evaluate the article. Does it include relevant and sufficient evidence? Does it avoid hasty generalizations? Is it reliable?

- _____

- _____

- _____

F **WRITE.** Write an evaluation of the article.

Remember to do each of the following:
- Summarize the article.
- Evaluate the source and writer.
- Assess whether the evidence is relevant and sufficient.
- Look for evidence of logical fallacies.
- Avoid hasty generalizations.
- Say whether you thought the article was reliable or unreliable.

G **REVISE.** Use the Writing Checklist to evaluate your writing and make revisions.

H **COLLABORATE.** Share your writing with a partner. Use any feedback to improve your writing.

I **PUBLISH.** Create a final document to share with others.

Writing Checklist	
	The text includes...
Structure:	✓ Evaluative essay
Organization:	✓ News story summary
	✓ Claim and evaluation
	✓ Conclusion
Word Choice:	✓ Academic words
	✓ Inference signal words
Writing Skill:	✓ Qualifiers to avoid hasty generalizations
Grammar:	✓ Modals of deduction
	✓ Adjective clauses

Lesson 10: Workplace Soft Skills

A **DEFINE. Complete the sentence.**

Taking initiative means that you _____.
- **a.** follow directions and are dependable
- **b.** take action and do things without being told to
- **c.** are kind and considerate to other people

B **EVALUATE. Read Situation 1 and the job applicant's response. Then answer the question.**

Situation 1

You are an IT technician and work at a small company that has an all-staff meeting every month. You notice that the meeting always requires a laptop, projector, and speakers, but no one has been assigned the task of setting them up. It's never done in advance, and someone is always setting up the equipment while people wait for the meeting to start.

What are the most and least effective ways of dealing with this situation?

Response	Most Effective	Least Effective
1. Complain to your colleagues about how much time is being wasted at the beginning of every meeting.	☐	☑
2. When people are struggling with the equipment at the next meeting, offer your assistance.	☐	☐
3. Write an email to your boss, asking him to choose someone to be in charge of setting up the equipment for future meetings.	☐	☐
4. Before the next meeting starts, set up the equipment so it's ready to go on time.	☑	☐

The applicant's response is effective because it recognizes that _____.
- **a.** the boss probably wants to be in charge of choosing someone for this kind of assignment
- **b.** there's not much that an individual employee can do to improve this situation
- **c.** it's appropriate to do the task yourself if it is currently no one's responsibility
- **d.** people prefer to keep doing things the way they have always been done

C **ASSESS. How does the applicant take initiative?**

_____

_____

_____

_____

Occupation Profile: Information technology (IT) technician

IT technicians provide computer support at many companies, both large and small. They may install computer networks, connect equipment such as projectors and printers, install software on individual computers, and answer employees' technical questions. Some IT technicians have a bachelor's degree in information technology; others have certifications in particular software. Employment in this field is expected to grow rapidly over the next 10 years.

D ANALYZE. Read Situation 2 and respond to the situation. Then answer the question.

Situation 2

You are an administrative assistant in an office that holds a staff event at a local park every year. Your boss asks you to call and book two buses to take people to the event. She gives you the phone number for a bus company she has used before, but when you call, they don't have any buses available.

What are the most and least effective ways of dealing with this situation?

Response	Most Effective	Least Effective
1. Send your boss an email saying that the bus company is booked.	☐	☐
2. Text some of your co-workers and ask them what they think you should do.	☐	☐
3. Avoid upsetting your boss and don't mention the situation until she brings it up.	☐	☐
4. Research other bus companies and send your boss information about their prices and availability.	☐	☐

My response is effective because it recognizes that _____.
  a. I should take the initiative to solve problems that come up
  b. notifying my boss of a problem shows enough initiative in this situation
  c. I should ask other people for help before I take initiative on my own
  d. taking initiative may not be the right thing to do in this situation

E APPLY. Describe a situation in which you have taken or would take initiative in the workplace.

_____

_____

_____

_____

_____

_____

_____

_____

_____

_____

_____

Occupation Profile: Administrative assistant

Administrative assistants handle many routine office tasks such as filing documents, answering phones, greeting visitors, ordering supplies, scheduling, and making travel arrangements. They are often expected to have an associate's degree and excellent computer skills. Bilingual skills may also be preferred. Employment in this area is expected to decline over the next 10 years.

Answer Key

UNIT 1

Page 2, Exercise A

1. Joy decided to consult with the career counselor at her college.
2. Min Hee enjoys helping patients in a hospital setting.
3. Dan needs to clarify some information before he makes a career choice.
4. Ken practiced talking about his aspirations before the interview.
5. Jun did not finish preparing for the interview until late last night.
6. Yuki would like to find a job that has potential for advancement.
7. Rosa hopes to major in a field she finds inherently interesting.
8. Feng plans to build her expertise by doing an internship.
9. Jean Paul expects to pursue a career in engineering.
10. Alexandra agreed to take several different assessments before the interview.
11. Amy prefers to work with a team. / Amy prefers working with a team.
12. Ari chose to focus on instructional design.

Page 3, Exercise B

(to find out) / finding out
to take / (taking)
(to get) / getting
to work / (working)
(to help) / helping
(to hire) / hiring
be / (being)
(to pay) / paying
(to pursue) / pursuing
to take / (taking)
to study / (studying)
to sit / (sitting)
to work / (working)
(to learn) / learning
(to study) / studying
(to take) / taking
to take / (taking)
to think / (thinking)

Page 4, Exercise B

1. T; line 3
2. F; line 4
3. T; lines 5–7
4. T; lines 12–13

Page 5, Exercise C

1. high school diploma
2. $24,500
3. 1,185,800
4. 3,253,000
5. $11.77

Page 6, Exercise A

1. a
2. *Examples:* for instance, for example

Page 7, Exercise C

1. F; line 12
2. F; line 16
3. T; lines 17–20
4. F; line 25

Page 7, Exercise D

1. b
2. a
3. b
4. c
5. a

Page 8, Exercise A

Alan began <u>working</u> as a server at a chain restaurant because he needed (to earn) some money. Initially, he didn't have any interest in the restaurant business. However, after a few years of <u>doing</u> the job, he began (to dream) about <u>becoming</u> a regional manager. Once a month, a regional manager came by (to talk) to Alan's boss and the employees. It was the regional manager's job (to oversee) all the restaurants in an area and make sure everyone was happy. Alan liked the idea of <u>traveling</u> and <u>talking</u> to people, but he wasn't sure about the requirements (to get) a job like that. After three years as a server, he decided it was time (to start) <u>working</u> toward his goal. <u>Getting</u> more information was the first item on his list, so Alan decided (to ask) his manager for a meeting (to discuss) his plans.

Page 8, Exercise B

1. Owning
2. setting
3. to acquire
4. to achieve
5. to establish
6. revising / to revise
7. consulting
8. to take
9. to achieve
10. to ask

Page 9, Exercise C

meeting; to talk
finding out
overseeing
becoming
asking; opening up; to apply;
moving up; making

Page 9, Exercise D

What are your long-term goals? Maybe you want to get a position in upper management or apply for a small business loan so you can start your own business. Maybe you just want to acquire a new skill. Whatever it is, not ~~to set~~ *setting* a time frame for a goal is a common mistake. People often plan on ~~get~~ *getting* around to something eventually, but without deadlines, it's hard to stick to those plans. Consider ~~put~~ *putting* your goals on a calendar so you can keep track of them. If you often have trouble ~~to meet~~ *meeting* your deadlines difficult, it may be that you are not setting realistic time frames. Be particularly careful with goals that need ~~being~~ *to be* coordinated. Challenge yourself, but don't expect ~~accomplishing~~ *to accomplish* the impossible!

Page 10, Exercise A

1. b
2. *Examples:* for instance, such as

Page 11, Exercise C

1. b
2. a
3. a
4. b
5. c

Page 11, Exercise D
1. 1,156
2. 371
3. 2015
4. 2019

Page 12, Exercise B
1. One of the most successful people I know is my friend Guillermo.
2. Did you know that more than 3,000,000 people die every year from drinking unsafe water?
3. Guillermo and his team help bring clean water to people.

Page 12, Exercise C
1. Did you know that more than 3,000,000 people die every year from drinking unsafe water?
2. Dirty water kills 5,000 children a day.
3. More than 30% of the world lacks access to clean drinking water.

Page 14, Exercise A
b

Page 14, Exercise B
a

Page 15, Exercise D
Most likely to Do=4
Least likely to Do=3

c

UNIT 2

Page 16, Exercise A
1. c
2. c
3. d
4. b
5. a
6. d

Page 16, Exercise B
should make sure / ought to make sure
may want to use / might want to use
should consider / ought to consider
shouldn't have
might be
could print / should print / ought to print

Page 17, Exercise C
Answers may vary.
should think
might want to contact
could ask
shouldn't make
may want to do

Page 17, Exercise D
Answers may vary.
1. You should ask your most recent employer to write you a job reference.
2. You might want to ask a co-worker you know well.
3. You shouldn't ask friends and family to be a job reference.
4. You may not want to ask an employer who wasn't happy with your work.
5. You ought to show your résumé to your job references.
6. You may want to make suggestions if you want them to mention specific skills.

Page 18, Exercise B
1. F; line 2
2. T; lines 8–9
3. T; line 13
4. F; lines 18–19

Page 19, Exercise C
1. b
2. a
3. c

Page 20, Exercise A
1. c
2. overall

Page 21, Exercise C
1. F; lines 6–7
2. T; lines 16–17
3. F; lines 18–19
4. T; line 26

Page 22, Exercise A
1. Jim has been working at a bank since 2016.
2. Hassan and Mia have been studying English for three years.
3. Some employees have not been behaving appropriately.
4. Victoria and Koji have obviously been trying to improve lately.

5. Jason's illness has been affecting his performance.

Page 22, Exercise B
1. I've been looking for work since November.
2. Since Ben has learned new computer skills, he is hoping for higher compensation.
3. Kamila has been studying Spanish since 2018.
4. Jenni has been taking computer classes since the fall.
5. Ms. Perez and Mr. Lee have interviewed four people for the job, and now they are done interviewing.
6. Since Roberto has practiced for his job interview, he now feels confident and ready.

Page 23, Exercise C
(have donated)/ have been donating
(has also started)/ has also been starting
have learned /(have been learning)
has grown /(has been growing)
(has expanded)/ has been expanding
(has helped)/ has been helping
(have worked)/ have been working
(have donated)/ have been donating

Page 23, Exercise D
has interviewed
has taken
have shown up
has been looking
have decided

Page 24, Exercise A
1. *Answers may vary:* It will be important to have technology-friendly transferable skills for jobs of the future.
2. *Example:* to sum up

Page 25 Exercise D
1. a; lines 7–9
2. b; lines 16–17
3. a; lines 18–19

Page 25, Exercise E
1. F
2. T
3. F

Answer Key

Page 26, Exercise B

Job Ad	Résumé
• replace parts, repair damaged parts	• Perform daily checks to replace or repair parts as needed.
• diagnose problems with aircraft, make suggestions for how to fix them	• Work with manager to diagnose and fix problems.
• keep reports on all the work you do	• Keep reports on all maintenance performed.

Page 28, Exercise A

c

Page 28, Exercise B

c

Page 29, Exercise D

Response	1	2	3	4
1. Apologize to customers and tell them you'll have the receptionist return their call.			✓	
2. Learn different ways to respond to customers' complaints and then practice until you become more confident.		✓		
3. Deal with customers' complaints as well as you can, even though it makes you uncomfortable.			✓	

4. Let the phone calls go to voicemail so the receptionist can deal with customers' complaints when she returns.				✓

c

UNIT 3

Page 30, Exercise A

1. ø
2. ø
3. more
4. more
5. ø
6. more

Page 30, Exercise B

more modern
more expensive
more carefully
harder
fewer
cheaper
more accurate
better

Page 31, Exercise C

Answers may vary.
1. The Red Card has a higher interest rate.
2. The Bank10 Card has a more generous cash-back program.
3. You can get approved faster for the Red Card.
4. You need better credit to apply for the Bank10 Card.
5. The Bank10 Card has a longer zero-interest period.
6. The Bank10 Card has a lower yearly fee.

Page 31, Exercise D

1. ~~more high~~ *higher*
2. ~~more rich~~ *richer*
3. ~~more quick~~ *quicker /* *more quickly*
4. ~~more big~~ *bigger*
5. ~~painfuller~~ *more painful*
6. ~~more bad~~ *worse*
7. ~~more easier~~ *more easily*
8. ~~importanter~~ *more important*

9. ~~more~~ *better*
10. ~~more happy~~ *happier*

Page 32, Exercise B

1. F; lines 10–11
2. T; lines 17–18
3. F; lines 19–20
4. T; lines 21–22

Page 33, Exercise C

1. Maria
2. Ben
3. Ben
4. Hana

Page 34, Exercise A

1. a
2. *Examples:* however, similar to, unlike, by contrast

Page 35, Exercise C

1. b; lines 11–12
2. c; lines 13–14
3. a; lines 19–20

Page 36, Exercise A

1. c
2. a
3. a
4. b
5. c
6. d

Page 36, Exercise B

the worst
the prettiest
the most embarrassing
the best
the most convincing
the lowest
the most affordable
the most expensive

Page 37, Exercise C

One of *the* best financial decisions I made last year was to buy a bike instead of a car. Rather than spending all my money for a down payment on the ~~cheaper~~ *cheapest* car I could find, I bought a very nice bike. The bike doesn't just save me money—it also saves me time! I compared the times for driving, taking the train, and riding my bike to work. Believe it or not, during rush hour, riding my bike is the ~~faster~~ *fastest*! I feel good about riding my bike to work because pollution from cars is one of the ~~most bad~~ *worst* things about this city, and it contributes to climate change. Finally, riding a bike almost every day has been great exercise. I'm the ~~healthy~~ *healthiest* I've ever been. Getting a bike wasn't just a great financial decision, it was one of the ~~more~~ smartest decisions I've ever made!

Page 37, Exercise D

1. The sedan is the oldest.
2. The compact is the most expensive.
3. The compact has the longest warranty.
4. The sedan has the highest mileage.
5. The sedan is the cheapest.
6. The hybrid is the most fuel efficient.

Page 38, Exercise A

1. The differences between working for yourself and for someone else
2. working for yourself and working for someone else

Page 39, Exercise C

1. a; line 6
2. c; lines 21–23
3. b; lines 24–25

Page 39, Exercise D

1. b
2. a
3. d
4. c

Page 40, Exercise B

both, also, similarly, by contrast, unlike, however

Page 42, Exercise A

b

Page 42, Exercise B

c

Page 43, Exercise D

	Response	Very Inappropriate	Slightly Inappropriate	Slightly Appropriate	Very Appropriate
1.	Tell the customer that her anger is misdirected because you don't make restaurant policy.		✓		
2.	Tell the customer that you're very sorry but you just aren't allowed to change the order.			✓	
3.	Tell the customer you understand how she feels and you'll see if the manager can make an exception.				✓
4.	Tell the customer that she has no right to treat people this way.	✓			

d

UNIT 4

Page 44, Exercise A

1. b
2. d
3. a
4. c
5. a
6. b
7. c
8. d

Page 44, Exercise B

1. a
2. b
3. a
4. a
5. b
6. b

Page 45, Exercise C

1. In order to get a job, Ann needs to improve her computer skills. / Ann needs to improve her computer skills in order to get a job.
2. The problem is complicated because it has many dimensions. / Because the problem has many dimensions, it's complicated.
3. Although May has no experience working with a team, she knows how to collaborate. / May knows how to collaborate, although she has no experience working with a team.
4. Pablo volunteered for committee work so that he could get experience.

Answer Key

5. Marta became team leader because of her people skills. / Because of her people skills, Marta became team leader.
6. Despite Sam's excellent communication skills, he is very shy. / Sam is very shy despite his excellent communication skills.
7. Even though Pia started the job recently, she has made a good impression on the boss. / Pia has made a good impression on the boss even though she started the job recently.
8. Jim lost his job due to his inflexible attitude. / Due to his inflexible attitude, Jim lost his job.

Page 45, Exercise D

1. Kara is going to get training in order to get a promotion.
2. Although it wasn't very good, I'm going to save my performance evaluation.
3. Due to his impressive résumé, Bo has received several job offers.
4. Because Anya works hard, she has moved quickly up the career ladder.
5. Even though she had a late start on her career, Rosa has advanced very quickly.
6. The store is seeking new employees because of a recent increase in sales.

Page 46, Exercise B

1. F; line 9
2. F; line 10
3. T; lines 14–15
4. T; lines 16–17

Page 47, Exercise C

1. d
2. c
3. a
4. b

Page 48, Exercise A

1. b
2. *Examples:* say, show, suggests, according to, indicate

Page 49, Exercise C

1. T; line 11
2. F; line 13
3. F; lines 22–24
4. T; lines 25–26

Page 49, Exercise D

Answers will vary.
1. It's lonely to work all day without co-workers.
2. Telecommuters miss out on professional development opportunities at work, such as trainings and seminars.
3. It's harder to develop teamwork skills when you telecommute.

Page 50, Exercise A

1. c
2. b
3. c
4. d
5. a
6. b

Page 50, Exercise B

1. Would you mind if I sit here?
2. Would you mind turning down your TV?
3. Would you mind not taking my water bottle?
4. Would you mind if I didn't go to the meeting?
5. Would you mind if I made a personal phone call?
6. Would you mind trying to be more consistent?
7. Would you mind if I didn't start the inventory until tomorrow?
8. Would you mind coming a few minutes early next time?

Page 51, Exercise C

Matt: Hey Emma. Would you mind ~~to help~~ *helping* Frank clean the tables?
Emma: Sure, but I'm pretty busy right now. Would you mind if I ~~do~~ *did* it in about 10 minutes?
Matt: That's fine. Thanks a lot for your cooperation.
Emma: Of course. By the way, would you mind if ~~I'm leaving~~ *I left* an hour early next Saturday? My sister is getting married. Carla said she can come

in early to cover my shift.
Matt: That's fine, but I need you and Carla to put the change in the scheduling app. It's company policy. Would you mind ~~take~~ *taking* care of that tonight?
Emma: Of course. We'll do it right away.

Page 51, Exercise D

Answers will vary.
1. Would you mind not singing?
2. Would you mind answering my phone while I'm out?
3. Would you mind if I didn't come to the meeting?
4. Would you mind contributing $3?
5. Would you mind if I borrowed your chair while you're out?
6. Would you mind not using the copy machine right now?

Page 52, Exercise A

1. to find out more about the organizational chart at Blue Leopard—who the people are and what their roles are
2. Blue Leopard helps companies design and develop new products.

Page 53, Exercise C

1. c; lines 2–6
2. b; line 19
3. a; line 24
4. b; line 28

Page 53, Exercise D

1. c
2. a
3. b
4. d
5. e

Page 54, Exercise B

Audience: Wanda's manager
Tone: formal, professional

Page 56, Exercise A

b

Page 56, Exercise B

b

Page 57, Exercise D

Most Effective = 4
Least Effective = 1

a

UNIT 5

Page 58, Exercise A

Homelessness has been increasing for decades, and it is a complicated problem <u>that requires more than one kind of solution</u>. Long-term affordable housing is the first issue <s>that</s> <u>we need to address</u>. Shelters provide protection for people <u>who are sleeping outside</u>, but that is only a temporary solution. Once homeless people are provided with long-term housing, they can access other services <u>that will help them make permanent changes</u>. For example, they can get the healthcare <s>that</s> <u>they need</u>. Long-term housing also gives people the stability <u>that is required for participating in job-training programs</u>. For homeless families, long-term housing often results in children <u>who stay in school and are more connected to their communities</u>. There are many nonprofit organizations <u>whose members are working hard to connect people with affordable housing</u>. Hopefully, their efforts will drastically reduce the number of people <u>who end up living on the streets or in shelters</u>.

Page 58, Exercise B

1. who
2. whose
3. that / which
4. that / which
5. who
6. that / which
7. that / which
8. whose
9. that / which
10. that / which

Page 59, Exercise C

that your organization does
who need it most
I have done
whose families can't provide
  everything they need

who needed things like food,
  clothing, and school supplies
that could help them
who had insufficient income to pay
  the rent
you were able to help

Page 59, Exercise D

1. She works for a nonprofit organization that <s>it</s> helps people find affordable housing.
2. There are some government subsidies <s>whom</s> *that* will help you pay your rent.
3. Yesterday, I talked to the neighbors *who* had been evicted from their apartment last year.
4. The organization helps people <s>whom</s> *who* have insufficient income.
5. It may be difficult to understand someone <s>who</s> *whose* problems are very different from your own.
6. This house needs a lot of repairs that I don't know how to do <s>them</s>.

Page 60, Exercise B

1. T; line 7
2. F; lines 10–11
3. T; lines 13–15
4. T; lines 15–16

Page 61, Exercise C

1. $1,450
2. $2,900
3. No.
4. He is.
5. six months

Page 62, Exercise A

1. a
2. *Examples:* address this issue, remedy

Page 63, Exercise C

1. F; lines 5–6
2. F; lines 11–12
3. T; lines 16–17
4. T; lines 23–24

Page 63, Exercise D

1. b
2. a
3. d
4. c

Page 63, Exercise E

Problem
Rental costs are rising more quckly than wages.

Problem
There are more houses for sale than there are available rental units.

Problem
Mortgage companies have tightened their lending laws.

Solution
States should adopt rental caps

Page 64, Exercise A

1. that was paid on the loan
   What was the total amount of interest paid on the loan?
2. that were rejected by banks
   The Smiths have had three loan applications rejected by banks.
3. that confirm our residency status
   We had to show them documents confirming our residency status.
4. that range from very low to very high
   You can find apartments here with rents ranging from very low to very high.
5. that is being offered this week
   We'd like to secure the rate being offered this week.
6. that are listed on the website
   Did you see the prices listed on the website?
7. who are buying the house down the street
   We talked to the people buying the house down the street.
8. that was earned during the last three years
   Please write down your gross income earned during the last three years.

Answer Key

Page 64, Exercise B

1. The loan officer described some problems encountered by many people.
2. People applying for loans may not realize their credit score is too low.
3. The interest rates advertised by the banks are often only for people with good credit.
4. There are many fees associated with buying a house.

Page 65, Exercise C

looking
being
paid
taken
written
applying
included
for rent

Page 65, Exercise D

1. There are some low-interest loans available to people with a good credit score.
2. The loan officer reviewed the documents submitted by the applicants.
3. The bank will offer low-interest rates to people earning a high income.
4. Charles was surprised by the amount of the loan approved by his bank.
5. Many homes are still unaffordable for people getting paid an average salary.

Page 66, Exercise A

1. how 3D printers could help countries build more affordable houses
2. *Examples:* cement, sand, metal, recycled plastic

Page 67, Exercise C

1. F; lines 2–3
2. T; lines 4–5
3. T; lines 17–18
4. F; lines 25–26

Page 67, Exercise D

Answers may vary.
1a. a lack of affordable housing around the world

1b. 1 billion people around the world lack adequate shelter. Millions of people in Central America don't have a safe place to live.
2a. 3D-printed houses
2b. They are cheap and can be built in one day for just $4,000. They are affordable, sustainable, and environmentally friendly.
3a. Yes
3b. Yes
3c. Yes
4. *Students' answers will vary.*

Page 68, Exercise B

1. Rent is too expensive.
2. Politicians should adopt rental cap laws.
3. Oregon passed a law to cap rent in 2019. Other states, such as California and New York, are planning to adopt similar laws.
4. the best solution is

Page 70, Exercise A

a

Page 70, Exercise B

d

Page 71, Exercise D

Most Likely to Do = 2
Least Likely to Do = 1

d

UNIT 6

Page 72, Exercise A

1. If
2. unless
3. if
4. unless
5. Unless
6. If

Page 72, Exercise B

1. c
2. b, d
3. c
4. a
5. c, d
6. a
7. b
8. a

9. b
10. b

Page 72, Exercise C

look, will see / can see
moves
will drop / are going to drop
don't have to go out
stay
changes
will continue / is going to continue
think, do
get, will go / can go
happens
have

Page 73, Exercise D

Answers will vary.
1. If there is a flash flood advisory, I'll cancel my plans.
2. If the roads are icy, I won't drive to class.
3. I'll go to the beach if it's sunny and hot next weekend.
4. Unless I fix my roof, my furniture is going to get wet.
5. I'm going to go shopping unless it starts snowing.
6. If the storm comes, I won't have anything to eat.
7. If the forecast is right, it will be a beautiful weekend.
8. Children will be happy if school closes because of snow.

Page 75, Exercise B

1. T; line 4
2. T; lines 6–8
3. F; lines 13–15
4. F; lines 17–19

Page 75, Exercise C

1. c
2. a
3. b

Page 76, Exercise A

1. b
2. Examples: consequently, cause, as a result

Page 77, Exercise C

1. T; lines 1–2
2. F; lines 10–11
3. F; lines 21–22
4. T; lines 27–28

Page 77, Exercise D

Answers may vary.

1.0–4.9	The earthquake will cause the ground to shake. A few objects might fall off the shelves.
5.0–6.9	The earthquake will damage buildings, cars, and streets.
7.0–7.9	The earthquake may cause whole buildings to collapse. People 100 miles away will feel the ground shake.
8.0–10.0	The earthquake will cause major damage to entire cities and towns.

Page 78, Exercise A

1. would assist
2. wouldn't take
3. closed
4. weren't
5. had
6. struck
7. felt
8. wouldn't be

Page 78, Exercise B

would happen
happened
broke
lost
suffered
would / could go
rose
didn't have
would be
came

Page 79, Exercise C

1. If this scenario actually happened, the city would be in trouble.
2. If the storm lasted another week, it would exceed our worst predictions.
3. If I moved to an area with lots of earthquakes, I would worry about them all the time.
4. What would you do if there were a hurricane during your vacation on the island?

5. How would they get back to their homes if the roads were flooded?
6. If we had another bad tornado here, I would probably move.

Page 79, Exercise D

1. If this house were in California, we ~~will~~ _would_ attach those bookcases to the wall.
2. If there ~~is~~ _were_ a hurricane next month, thousands of tourists would be stranded.
3. The insurance ~~isn't~~ _wouldn't be_ so expensive if this weren't a flood-prone area.
4. If we ~~don't~~ _didn't_ have so many big storms in this area, people wouldn't be so prepared.
5. I would keep plenty of emergency supplies in my basement if I ~~live~~ _lived_ here.
6. Hurricanes would affect this town more if it ~~isn't~~ _weren't_ sheltered by the large bay.

Page 80, Exercise A

1. why Indonesia has more earthquakes than any other country
2. A fault line is a crack in the earth where plates shift and smash into each other.

Page 81, Exercise D

1. a; line 1
2. b; lines 12–14
3. c; lines 20–21
4. b; lines 24–25

Page 82, Exercise B

Complex sentence: Engineers are working to develop buildings that can survive earthquakes.

Compound sentence: These buildings kill people when they fall, and they cost billions of dollars in damage.

Page 84, Exercise A

c

Page 84, Exercise B

b

Page 85, Exercise D

Response	1	2	3	4
1. Speak loudly so you can get everyone's attention for the issue you want to discuss.			✓	
2. Raise your hand and ask everyone to take turns speaking about the issues that concern them.		✓		
3. Keep quiet and look at your phone for the rest of the meeting since nothing is getting accomplished anyway.				✓
4. Make an agenda and ask your coworkers to take turns discussing one item at a time.	✓			

c

UNIT 7

Page 86, Exercise A

1. provided
2. whether
3. Should
4. As
5. only
6. condition
7. long
8. Even

Page 86, Exercise B

1. a, b
2. a, b, d
3. b, d
4. a, c, d
5. a, b
6. a
7. c, d
8. a, c, d

Answer Key

Page 87, Exercise C

1. Only if we lower out fossil fuel consumption will global warming begin to slow down.
2. Even if you can't afford to buy an electric car, there are other things you can do.
3. You can limit your greenhouse gas emissions provided that you put a little effort into it.
4. Whether or not individuals change their behavior, governments and corporations need to address climate change.
5. As long as humanity works together to take this problem seriously, we can make the future better for our children.
6. Climate change is attributed to human behavior, so we can slow it down on the condition that we change our behavior.

Page 87, Exercise D

1. As long as people begin to recycle more, there will be less waste in landfills.
2. Provided that some areas continue to experience less rainfall, desertification will increase.
3. Even if water pollution is cleaned up, overfishing will still be a problem.
4. Planting trees will help absorb carbon dioxide on the condition that we don't cut down as many as we plant.
5. Should we do nothing to combat climate change, the planet may warm by as much as 5 degrees by 2100.
6. The city has special bins to encourage people to compost whether or not they have a garden.

Page 88, Exercise B

1. F; line 4
2. T; lines 6–7
3. F; line 11
4. T; lines 13–14

Page 89, Exercise C

1. b
2. a
3. c

Page 90, Exercise A

1. c
2. *Examples:* primary, noteworthy, critical

Page 91, Exercise C

1. F; lines 1–2
2. F; lines 2–3
3. T; lines 11–12
4. T; lines 22–24

Page 91, Exercise D

1. a
2. c
3. b

Page 92, Exercise A

1. b
2. a
3. c
4. c
5. c
6. b

Page 92, Exercise B

1. had banned, would/could have prevented
2. would/could have spent, had replaced
3. had bought, wouldn't have had, had driven, wouldn't have been
4. would/could have saved, had called
5. had ridden, would have used

Page 93, Exercise C

1. had gotten a raise, she would have bought a hybrid.
   have bought a hybrid if she had gotten a raise.
2. known about the new recycling center, she would have recycled her batteries.
   have recycled her batteries if she had known about the new recycling center.
3. had told Omar and Irma about the recycling center, they would have taken their bottles there.
   have taken their bottles to the recycling center if Yolanda had told them about it.
4. had fit her cousin, she would have given them to her.
   have given her clothes to her cousin if they had fit her.

5. had gotten a job closer to home, he wouldn't have to drive so much.
   have to drive so much if he had gotten a job closer to home.
6. had brought glass containers instead of non-recyclable ones, we would be able to recycle them.
   be able to recycle the containers if our friends had brought glass ones instead of non-recyclable ones.

Page 93, Exercise D

1. Passenger pigeons wouldn't have gone extinct in 1914 if they hadn't been widely hunted by humans.
2. If people hadn't diverted water from Great Salt Lake, it wouldn't have almost disappeared.
3. If the government hadn't banned hunting the bald eagle, it could have disappeared.
4. If European governments hadn't created strict laws about sustainable forestry, the area that is covered by forests wouldn't have increased.
5. California's fires in 2019 wouldn't have been as terrible if there hadn't been so many years of drought.
6. If people hadn't cut down so many trees and plants, there wouldn't have been terrible mudslides.

Page 94, Exercise A

1. how to use batteries to store solar energy
2. Solar power can only be produced during the day when it's sunny, but peak demand is at night. The power needs to be stored in a battery if it's going to be used later.

Page 95, Exercise C

1. F; lines 1–2
2. F; line 7
3. T; lines 12–13
4. T; lines 19–20

Page 95, Exercise D

1. b
2. d
3. a
4. c

Page 96, Exercise B

1. point
2. claim
3. evidence

Page 96, Exercise C

Article A
1. More people should think about buying hydrogen fuel cell cars.
2. The car doesn't rely on a battery. Hydrogen fuel cell cars can drive longer distances than electric cars.
3. They can charge in five minutes. They can drive about 300 miles before they need to be charged again.

Page 98, Exercise A

c

Page 98, Exercise B

a

Page 99, Exercise D

Undesirable = 4
Slightly Undesirable = 1
Slightly Desirable = 2
Desirable = 3

d

UNIT 8

Page 100, Exercise A

1. a, b
2. b, c
3. a, b, d
4. c, d
5. b
6. a, c
7. b, c, d
8. c, d

Page 100, Exercise B

will completely replace
will be / is going to be
will get better / are going to get better
will be / are going to be

will need / are going to need
won't be able / aren't going to be able
won't be / isn't going to be
will be doing / will do / are going to do

Page 101, Exercise C

When people ~~will~~ hear the stories about intelligent robots taking over jobs, they often wonder what humans are going to do for work in the future. Robots have already taken over many jobs that humans used to do, but what will happen when they ~~will~~ start doing more? According to many experts, intelligent machines will someday be ~~diagnose~~ _diagnosing_ most of our illnesses. They will _be_ teaching most of our children online and arguing for us in court. They ~~are~~ _will_ even be producing a lot of our art and music. In most cases, AI will do a part of every job, but it ~~doesn't~~ _won't_ eliminate the job completely. For example, AI is getting better and better at diagnosis, but patients will probably want a human doctor at their bedside for the foreseeable future.

Page 102, Exercise B

1. T; line 1
2. F; lines 6–7
3. T; lines 17–19
4. T; lines 23–24

Page 103, Exercise C

1. b
2. a
3. c

Page 104, Exercise A

1. a
2. _Examples:_ as such, for this reason, ultimately, all in all

Page 105, Exercise C

1. T; lines 2–3
2. F; line 7
3. T; line 14
4. F; lines 20–22

Page 105, Exercise D

1. Yes, the address begins with https.
2. There is a lock symbol next to the web address.

Page 105, Exercise E

1. a
2. c
3. c

Page 106, Exercise A

1. wasn't working, had left, had started, hadn't gotten
2. weren't, had found
3. was driving, didn't have, looked, had stopped
4. told, didn't want
5. was going, had already pulled out
6. had purchased, was

Page 106, Exercise B

were walking
bumped
had happened
didn't apologize
was texting
didn't see
ran
hadn't noticed
were
resulted

Page 108, Exercise A

1. why children shouldn't have phones in the classroom
2. _Example:_ Students use their phones to text, email, and check social media accounts when they should be listening to the teacher.

Page 109, Exercise C

Answers may vary.

Most students have phones these days.	• More than half of students in grades K–8 have phones. • More than 80% of high school students have phones. • A whopping 99% of college students have phones.

Answer Key

Students should not be able to bring phones into the classroom.	• When they are allowed to bring their phones into class, students spend as much as 20% of class time texting, emailing, and checking their social media accounts. • The average student checks his or her phone 11 times during the school day. • Nearly 35% of teenagers admit to having used their phones to cheat on homework or tests.
Many schools have policies around phone use but they face resistance from parents.	• Almost 90% of schools in the United States have policies about phone use. • Of these schools, 63% allow students to have their phones at school but not in the classroom. • Almost half of all parents say they use their children's phones to track them.

Page 109, Exercise D

1. c
2. a
3. b

Page 110, Exercise B

On average, they are 552% more expensive than new print books. Almost 80% of students aged 8–18 multitask while using digital media.

1. Students shouldn't use tablets in the classroom.
2. Yes; the evidence is related to and supports the writer's claim.
3. Yes; the writer introduces a lot of evidence, and it's enough to convince me of the argument.

Page 112, Exercise A

b

Page 112, Exercise B

b

Page 113, Exercise D

Most Appropriate = 4
Least Appropriate = 2

c

UNIT 9

Page 114, Exercise A

A new yoga class is being offered at Silver Gym. This is a beginner's class for people of all shapes, sizes, and flexibility levels. Our instructors have received extensive training in both yoga and physical therapy. It can be scary to try something new, but in this class, you will be gently guided through the exercises by your instructors, and you will never be pushed to do something that is too difficult for you. All our classes are backed by a money-back guarantee. If you aren't satisfied after the first two classes, your money will be returned, no questions asked! So come on in and give yoga a try!

Page 114, Exercise B

is recommended
is being repaired
was modified
was being remodeled
has been maintained
will be replaced
should be posted
might be removed

Page 114, Exercise C

1. is
2. can
3. are
4. added

Page 115, Exercise D

1. Everyone is encouraged to eat unprocessed foods and get plenty of exercise and sleep.
2. The employees were given a discount on health insurance for going to the gym.
3. We were made aware of a problem with the food.
4. The gym will be reopened next month.

5. Yoga classes have been offered at this gym for several years.
6. Too many premature decisions have been made in the past.

Page 115, Exercise E

1. won't be served / aren't going to be served
   be made
   be found
   were consulted
   were made
2. was installed
   were put in
   was fixed up
   were placed
   was paid
   was approved

Page 116, Exercise B

1. T; lines 3, 15–16
2. T; line 11
3. F; lines 14–15
4. F; lines 19–20

Page 117, Exercise C

1. c
2. b
3. c
4. a

Page 118, Exercise A

1. c
2. Examples: experts say, in fact, research shows, in my opinion, I think, I believe

Page 119, Exercise C

1. F; line 4
2. T; lines 10–11
3. T; lines 15–16
4. F; lines 25–27

Page 119, Exercise D

1. a
2. b
3. a

Page 120, Exercise A

A lot of research has been done on mental health in recent years, and the evidence is growing that not getting enough sleep can have a negative effect on mental health. Researchers have found that sleep problems are common in patients with anxiety and depression. Sometimes, difficulty sleeping is a symptom of those conditions, but in some cases, anxiety and depression (are caused) by sleep problems. Sleep also affects learning. In one study, participants (were taught) a skill and then some of them (were deprived) of sleep. Participants who didn't sleep were unable to remember the skill the next day. The same skill (was remembered) easily by participants who got a good night's sleep.

Page 120, Exercise B

1. A; f
2. P; a
3. A; g
4. P; e
5. A; h
6. A; b
7. P; d
8. P; c

Page 120, Exercise C

make
causes
experience
are experienced
are made
is caused
harm
have been harmed / are harmed

Page 121, Exercise D

checked: b, c, d, f, i, j
1. This paper was written by two famous psychologists.
2. Several studies were conducted on this topic last year by scientists.
3. Some symptoms of anxiety can be relieved by relaxation techniques.
4. Sara's mood is often improved by exercise.
5. How is depression diagnosed?
6. Which exercises are recommended for relaxation?

Page 121, Exercise E

1. Jim was treated by a therapist for three years.
   A therapist treated Jim for three years.
2. Counseling helped Ann a lot.
   Ann was helped a lot by counseling.

3. Beautiful music always lifts his mood.
   His mood is always lifted by beautiful music.
4. Tom's job causes stress.
   Tom's stress is caused by his job.
5. Experts do not recommend a high-fat diet.
   A high-fat diet is not recommended by experts.
6. The light from her phone disturbed Kelly's sleep.
   Kelly's sleep was disturbed by the light from her phone.

Page 122, Exercise A

1. why more and more people will get arthritis
2. osteoarthritis and rheumatoid arthritis

Page 123, Exercise C

1. a
2. b
3. c

Page 123, Exercise D

1. b
2. c
3. a

Page 126, Exercise A

b

Page 126, Exercise B

d

Page 127, Exercise D

Most Likely = 4
Least Likely = 2

a

UNIT 10

Page 128, Exercise A

Dr. Cole: Good morning, Mr. Mun. How can I help you today?
Mr. Mun: Well, I've been feeling really tired lately, and I'm not sure what's causing it.
Dr. Cole: How long have you been feeling like this?
Mr. Mun: About three months.

Dr. Cole: OK. And can you tell me what your sleep schedule is like? Do you get enough sleep at night?
Mr. Mun: No, I don't. I go to bed at midnight and get up at 6 a.m.
Dr. Cole: That is definitely not enough sleep. Do you remember when you started sleeping for six hours a night?
Mr. Mun: Yeah. Three months ago. That's when I started working two jobs.
Dr. Cole: OK, Mr. Mun. I think I know why you're tired all the time!
Mr. Mun: Please tell me how I can get my energy back.
Dr. Cole: I'm sorry. I'm afraid you just have to get more sleep. Can you take a nap between jobs?
Mr. Mun: Maybe. I guess I'll try.

Page 128, Exercise B

1. Do you know how long he has had blurred vision?
2. I'm not sure when I was evaluated for diabetes.
3. I wonder how the oncologist treats a cancerous tumor.
4. Can you tell me how you got this injury?
5. I don't know why he was reluctant to meet with a specialist.
6. He has no idea when his blood pressure started going up.
7. Can you tell me who you were speaking to at the doctor's office?
8. The ophthalmologist isn't sure how she can treat my blurred vision.
9. Do you know what they'll give me for high blood pressure?
10. The optometrist doesn't know what is causing her distorted vision.

Page 129, Exercise C

Answers will vary.
1. Can you tell me who Don's cardiologist is?

Answer Key

2. Do you know what time my appointment with the dermatologist is?
3. I wonder how long he has been seeing the oncologist.
4. I don't know when she will have surgery.
5. I'm not sure what can cause blurred vision.
6. Do you know how often he confers with a specialist?
7. Could you tell me when the neurologist gets into the office?
8. I don't remember how he got that knee injury.

Page 129, Exercise D

Answers will vary.
where Kate is
what's wrong with her
what her phone number is
how late it's open
what they're called
how much it would cost

Page 130, Exercise B

1. F; line 8
2. T; lines 12–13
3. F; lines 17–18
4. F; line 25

Page 131, Exercise C

1. a
2. c
3. b

Page 131, Exercise D

1. d
2. c
3. b
4. a

Page 132, Exercise A

1. b
2. *Examples:* given that, therefore, consequently

Page 133, Exercise C

1. T; lines 2–3
2. T; lines 6–7
3. F; line 6
4. F; lines 24–25

Page 133, Exercise D

	Evidence	Lines
Premise 1	• The biggest problem with healthcare in the United States is that 9% of people lack any kind of insurance.	10–11
	• They worry it will be too expensive. A single prescription medicine can cost hundreds of dollars. A visit to the emergency room can cost thousands of dollars.	12–14
Premise 2	• Singaporeans can choose to get insurance either through the government or from private companies.	18–20
	• The country caps the price of prescription drugs.	21

Page 133, Exercise E

1. b
2. a
3. c

Page 134, Exercise A

Check the following:
1. Can you tell me if his residency begins next year?
2. I need to know if prescription drugs are covered by this plan.
3. I'd like to know whether or not the government regulates the price of medical procedures.
4. Can you tell me if they've covered the administrative costs of the program or not?
5. I wonder whether the pharmaceutical company paid for the research.

Page 134, Exercise B

1. if
2. whether
3. is

4. regulate
5. not
6. or
7. Do
8. followed

Page 135, Exercise C

Answers will vary.
1. I don't know if there are a lot of components to this problem.
2. Can you tell me if the insurance is going to cover my surgery?
3. Do you know whether the optometrist accepts this insurance?
4. I'm not sure if these tests are really necessary.
5. I need to know if you get health coverage through your job not.
6. Let me know whether you have seen the doctor in the last year.

Page 135, Exercise D

Answers will vary.
1. I'd like to know if I can pay this bill next month. Could you tell me whether I can pay this bill next month?
2. Can you tell me if the optometrist sees patients on weekends? I'd like to know whether the optometrist sees patients on weekends.
3. I'm wondering if you're going to send my refund soon. Could you tell me whether you're going to send my refund soon?
4. I'm not sure if I already paid my insurance bill. I don't know whether or not I paid my insurance bill.

Page 136, Exercise A

1. how we need to lower Medicare costs
2. four

Page 137, Exercise C

Answers will vary.

PART B
Premise 1: Doctor's visits are too expensive.
Premise 2: The government could invest in telemedicine. Doctors could help patients over the phone or video. These appointments would be shorter and less expensive.

Conclusion: Telemedicine would lower the costs of Medicare Part B.

PART C
Premise 1: People have limited private insurance options in part C.
Premise 2: The government could offer more private insurance options. People could pay extra to upgrade their care.
Conclusion: More options for private insurance would lower the costs of Medicare Part C.

PART D
Premise 1: The government spends too much on prescription drugs. It is the fastest growing Medicare cost.
Premise 2: The government should negotiate drug prices with drug companies.
Conclusion: Negotiating drug prices would lower the costs of Medicare part D.

Page 137, Exercise D
1. 28.1 million
2. 81.5 million
3. 2000

Page 138, Exercise B
Answers will vary.

Sentence Fragments
1. If we don't, we will run out of money.
2. If older people had more private insurance options, more Baby Boomers could afford to buy their own insurance.

Run-on Sentences
1. Millions of people are covered by Medicare, and that number is only going to increase in the next decade.
2. They don't fill prescriptions they need, and they take less medicine than they need to make it last longer.

Page 140, Exercise A
a

Page 140, Exercise B
b

Page 141, Exercise D

Response	1	2	3	4
1. Tell the employees to call the manager since she was the one who made changes. Explain that she interfered with your job and that you are angry about it.				✓
2. Tell the employees that you will take their complaints under consideration. Call the manager in private and explain that the situation has caused problems. Ask for advice about how to deal with it.			✓	
3. Tell the employees that you will call the manager since she is the one who made the changes. Ask the manager if you can change the schedule back.		✓		
4. Call the manager and discuss the changes. Tell her that she shouldn't have changed the schedule without talking to you first.	✓			

d

UNIT 11

Page 142, Exercise A

My cousin Margarita moved to the United States seven years ago, and today I attended her naturalization ceremony. Margarita has wanted to become a citizen since she came here, but the application process takes a long time. First, she had to get a residency card and legally reside in the United States for five years. After the five-year period had passed, she was able to submit an application along with a fee. She received an interview appointment several months later. The interview was conducted at a USCIS office, and it included an English test and ten U.S. history and government questions. Margarita received the interviewer's recommendation for approval, and today I watched her take the Oath of Allegiance and pledge her loyalty to the U.S. Constitution. It was a great day. Unfortunately, Margarita's parents, my aunt and uncle, still live in El Salvador, and they weren't able to attend today's ceremony. Hopefully, they can visit soon to celebrate.

Page 142, Exercise B
1. ten-year
2. children's
3. Brown's
4. boys'
5. citizen's
6. 71-year-old

Page 142, Exercise C
1. a
2. c
3. c
4. a
5. c
6. b

Page 143, Exercise D
movie
Amaya's
government
downtown
two-hour
ticket
parents'
train

Page 143, Exercise E
Answers will vary.
1. The naturalization process takes a long time.
2. I answered all of the interviewer's questions.

Answer Key

3. The immigration officer was very friendly.
4. The English requirement wasn't hard to meet.
5. The immigrants' applications were approved.

Page 145, Exercise B

1. T; line 7
2. F; line 13
3. F; lines 19–20
4. T; line 23

Page 145, Exercise C

1. a
2. c
3. d
4. b

Page 146, Exercise A

1. a
2. *Examples:* first, then, finally, during, last

Page 147, Exercise C

1. T; lines 3–4
2. F; lines 10–11
3. T; lines 18–19
4. T; lines 28–29

Page 147, Exercise D

1. before
2. before
3. after

Page 148, Exercise A

1. disappointing, disappointed
2. convincing, convinced
3. damaged, damaging
4. worried, worrying

Page 148, Exercise B

excited
tired
exciting
inspiring
disgusted
disgusting
making
interesting
convinced
disappointed

Page 149, Exercise C

Answers will vary.
1. George Washington served during a very challenging time in U.S. history.

2. Washington was exhausted after the Revolutionary War and the Philadelphia Convention.
3. Washington was concerned about leaving office.
4. Washington tolerated opposing views.
5. Visitors are frustrated because the United States doesn't use the metric system.
6. The petitioners were disappointed because manufacturers opposed the change.
7. Proponents of the metric system were pleased when product labels began using both units.
8. Some people were encouraged when NASA decided to use metric units.

Page 150, Exercise A

1. how a bill becomes a law
2. the House of Representatives

Page 151, Exercise C

(Before) a bill can become a law, it must be discussed and approved by the House of Representatives. (Then) it must be discussed and approved by the Senate. (Finally) the president of the United States must approve the bill. (Once) the president approves the bill, it becomes a law. (When) representatives have an idea for a bill, they do research on it. (Next) they find someone to sponsor the bill. (Next) the representative tries to get support for the bill… (Once) a bill has a sponsor and support, it is ready to be introduced. (Then) the sponsor puts it in a special box in the House of Representatives. (After) it has been put in the hopper, a clerk takes it out and reads it aloud to the representatives. The bill is (then) sent to a committee. (Once) the committee feels the bill is ready, it introduces it to the House. (When) the changes have been made, the representatives vote on the bill.

Page 151, Exercise D

1. c
2. a
3. d
4. b

Page 151, Exercise E

1. 435
2. 218
3. 100
4. 51

Page 154, Exercise A

b

Page 154, Exercise B

c

Page 155, Exercise D

Very Inappropriate = 1
Somewhat Inappropriate = 2
Somewhat Appropriate = 4
Very Appropriate = 3

b

UNIT 12

Page 156, Exercise A

1. c
2. a
3. c
4. a
5. b
6. a
7. a
8. d
9. b

Page 156, Exercise B

1. Tim said he would be at the meeting, but he must not *have* come. I didn't see him there.
2. Jean crossed the street outside of a crosswalk and got a ticket. That must ~~been~~ *be* illegal.
3. I didn't get my sample ballot in the mail. I must ~~forgot~~ *have forgotten* to register to vote.
4. Look at all those people in the street! They must *be* having some kind of demonstration.
5. Sara can't ~~write~~ *have written* this letter. It's full of mistakes, and she's always very careful.
6. Shawn said he saw Alice in court, but it couldn't ~~be~~ *have*

<u>been</u> her. She was at work all day.
7. There's a moving truck outside. Someone must finally <u>be</u> moving into the house next door.
8. I don't know what time he left last night. It may ~~be~~ *have been* around 10:00.

Page 157, Exercise C

1. must not have known
2. must be planning
3. might not understand
4. may have paid
5. may believe
6. can't have predicted
7. must not have made
8. may be talking

Page 158, Exercise B

1. F; lines 4–5
2. T; lines 7–8
3. F; lines 12–13
4. T; lines 14–15

Page 159, Exercise C

1. c
2. d
3. b
4. a

Page 160, Exercise A

1. b
2. *Examples:* infer, believe, guess

Page 161, Exercise C

1. T; lines 7–8
2. F; line 19
3. T; lines 28–30
4. F; lines 34–35

Page 161, Exercise D

1. a
2. b
3. b

Page 161, Exercise E

1. c
2. a
3. b

Page 162, Exercise A

The words of a Miranda warning, <u>which is given to anyone who is suspected of a crime and is going to be questioned,</u> vary from state to state. However, the warning always contains sentences that

say something like this: *You have the right to have an attorney present during questioning. If you cannot afford an attorney, one will be appointed for you.* This part of the Miranda warning refers to a right <u>that is guaranteed by the Sixth Amendment</u>: the right to counsel. People <u>who cannot afford to pay for a defense attorney</u> are represented by public defenders, <u>who are lawyers that work for a publicly funded part of the government</u>. In some places, the courts appoint private lawyers <u>who have agreed to accept these cases</u>.

Page 162, Exercise B

that Dave made
that was flashing its lights
who were following him
who had gotten out of the police car
, who had never been stopped before,
, which was in the glove compartment with a lot of junk

Page 163, Exercise C

1. The legal protections, ~~which~~ we receive from the Fifth Amendment are very important.
2. The man's confession, **which** ~~that~~ was difficult to believe, was thrown out of court.
3. *(checked)*
4. We are seeking justice for Nelson, **who** ~~that~~ was accused of a crime he did not commit.
5. *(checked)*
6. Mark, who lives next door to me, has many misconceptions about the law.

Page 163, Exercise D

1. The first part of a Miranda warning refers to rights that are guaranteed in the Fifth Amendment.
2. The Fifth Amendment, which is part of the Bill of Rights, addresses criminal procedure.
3. There is one section that says everyone has the right to "due process of law."
4. A person who has been accused of committing a crime cannot be forced to testify in court.
5. That person may refuse to provide any answers that might suggest they did something illegal.
6. A person who refuses to answer questions is "pleading the Fifth."

Page 164, Exercise A

1. reasons why voting should be mandatory
2. Voting should be mandatory.

Page 165, Exercise C

1. c
2. a
3. d
4. b

Page 165, Exercise D

1. b
2. a
3. c

Page 166, Exercise A

Answers will vary.
1. Some people don't care about the environment. However, we will probably elect politicians who will make laws that protect the environment at some point.
2. Few people are in favor of the bill to build a new airport, so it's likely it's never going to be built.

Page 166, Exercise C

Paper ballots can't be hacked.
It's not likely that paper ballots can be hacked.

Page 168, Exercise A

b

Page 168, Exercise B

c

Page 169, Exercise D

Most Effective = 4
Least Effective = 3

a

Credits

Cover

Mike Harrington/Stone/Getty Images (main image);
Moof/Cultura/Getty Images (top left); Thomas Barwick/
Digital Vision/Getty Images (top right).

Main Text

Page 3: Mentatdgt/Shutterstock; 4 (top): Katarzyna
Białasiewicz/123RF; 4 (bottom): GaudiLab/Shutterstock;
6: Michaeljung/Shutterstock; 8: Ferli/123RF; 14:
Nestor Rizhniak/Shutterstock; 15: Wavebreak Media
Ltd/123RF; 18: ImageFlow/Shutterstock; 19: Dmitrii
Vlasov/123RF; 20: FS Stock/Shutterstock; 23: Atelier
KNOX/Shutterstock; 28: Caftor/Shutterstock; 29: Elena
Elisseeva/Shutterstock; 30: D13/Shutterstock; 31(left):
Juksy/Shutterstock; 31(right): Chris77ho/123RF;
32: FtLaud/Shutterstock; 34: Igor Kardasov/123RF;
37(bicyclist): Connel/Shutterstock; 37 (red sedan):
Hennadii Tantsiura/Shutterstock; 37 (orange hybrid):
Rawpixel/123RF; 37 (blue compact): Dimitris Leonidas/
Shutterstock; 42: Diego Cervo/Shutterstock; 43:
Branislav Nenin/123RF; 46: Michaeljung/Shutterstock;
48: Metamorworks/Shutterstock; 51: Paul Vasarhelyi/
Shutterstock; 56: Craig Robinson/123RF; 57:
Imtmphoto/123RF; 60: Pormezz/Shutterstock; 66:
Imaginechina Limited/Alamy Stock Photo; 70: Cathy
Yeulet/123RF; 71: Fiphoto/Shutterstock; 73: Mr Twister/
Shutterstock; 74: SpeedShutter/Shutterstock; 84:
Katarzyna Białasiewicz/123RF; 85: Shutterstock; 90:
ZUMA Press, Inc./Alamy Stock Photo; 98: Kzenon/
Shutterstock; 99: Trekandshoot/Shutterstock; 107:
Antonio Guillem/Shutterstock; 112: Baloncici/
Shutterstock; 113: YIUCHEUNG/Shutterstock; 118:
MinDof/Shutterstock; 119: Julief514/123RF; 121: Dmitriy
Shironosov/123RF; 126: Stuart Jenner/Shutterstock;
127: Renovacio/Shutterstock; 129: Natika/123RF; 130:
Outline205/123RF; 131(left): Pabkov/Shutterstock;
131(right): Bayanova Svetlana/Shutterstock; 140: Tyler
Olson/123RF; 141: Dinis Tolipov/123RF; 145: Samuel
Borges Photography/Shutterstock; 146: Vladislav Gajic/
Shutterstock; 149: Everett Historical/Shutterstock;
154: Dmitry Kalinovsky/Shutterstock; 155: Mavo/
Shutterstock; 157: Diego Vito Cervo/123RF; 162: Lisa
F/Young/Shutterstock; 164: Peeradach Rattanakoses/
Shutterstock; 168: Sunshine Studio/Shutterstock; 169:
Aleksandr Davydov/123RF.